Department of Transport

Scottish Development Department

Welsh Office

Department of the Environment for Northern Ireland

METHOD OF MEASUREMENT FOR HIGHWAY WORKS

London: HMSO

JULY 1987

© Crown copyright 1987

Applications for reproduction should be made to HMSO

First published 1971

Third Edition 1987

Fourth impression 1990

ISBN 0 11 550808 2

CONTENTS

Part I

Definitions

Definitions

1 In this document entitled Method of Measurement for Highway Works (hereinafter referred to as "the Method of Measurement") unless the context otherwise requires, the following words and expressions shall have the meanings hereby respectively assigned to them, that is to say:

(a) "Conditions of Contract" means the Conditions of Contract referred to in the Tender;

(b) words and expressions to which meanings are assigned in the Conditions of Contract have the same meanings in the Method of Measurement;

(c) words and expressions to which meanings are assigned in the Specification and Drawings referred to in the Conditions of Contract have the same meanings in the Method of Measurement;

(d) "Bill of Quantities" means a list of items giving brief identifying descriptions and estimated quantities of work comprised in the execution of the works to be performed;

(e) Items designated "Provisional" are items for which the quantities of work to be executed cannot be determined with the same degree of accuracy as other items but for which it is deemed necessary to make provision;

(f) "Preliminary Item" means an item in respect of works, general obligations and risks antecedent to or involved in the execution of the Contract and which is set out in a "Preliminaries" section of the Bill of Quantities;

(g) "Finishings" means the miscellaneous surfacings, furniture and ancillary features that are added to any part of a structure;

(h) "Existing Ground Level" means the level of the ground before any work under the Contract is carried out.

(i) "Hard Material" is defined as:

    (i) material which requires the use of blasting, breakers or splitters for its removal but excluding individual masses less than 0.20 cubic metres;

    (ii) those strata or deposits so designated in the Contract.

(k) "Culvert" means an enclosed channel or pipe designated as a culvert in the Contract.

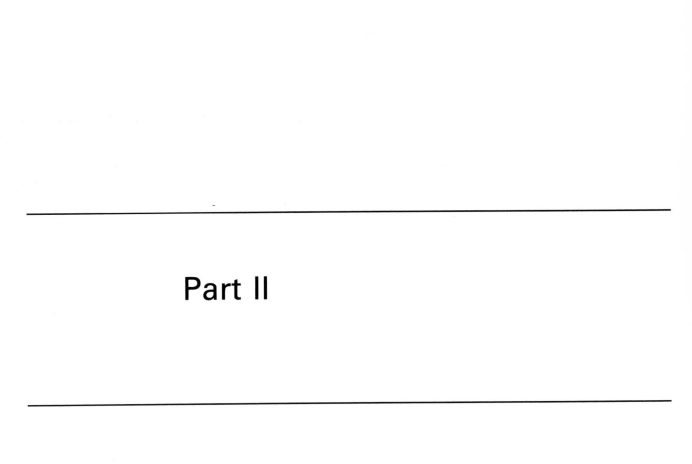

Part II

General Principles

General Principles

Method of Measurement   **1**   (a)   The Method of Measurement is intended for use for highway contracts based on the ICE Conditions of Contract. The use of the Method of Measurement requires appropriate amendment to Clause 57 of the Conditions and to the Appendix to the Form of Tender. If it is intended to use the Method of Measurement with other Conditions of Contract amendments will be required to the Method of Measurement.

(b)   The Method of Measurement is based on the 1986 edition of the Specification for Highway Works and the Highway Construction Details and on the principle that full details of construction requirements are provided in the Contract. Additions or amendments to the Specification for Highway Works or the Highway Construction Details which are not adequately covered by the Method of Measurement will necessitate appropriate amendment to suit. Provision is made in Part III—Preambles to Bill of Quantities, "Amendment to Method of Measurement" to accommodate such amendments.

Bill of Quantities   **2**   (a)   In the Bill of Quantities the sub headings and item descriptions identify the work covered by the respective items, read in conjunction with the matters listed against the relevant marginal headings "Item Coverage" in Part IV of the Method of Measurement, Part III Preambles to Bill of Quantities and amendments. The nature and extent of the work to be performed is to be ascertained by reference to the Drawings, Specification, Highway Construction Details and Conditions of Contract.

(b)   Items included in the Bill of Quantities for work to be executed or goods, materials or services to be supplied by a Nominated Sub Contractor shall be followed by separate items for:–
(i)   Labours in connection therewith in the form of a lump sum.
(ii)   All other charges and profit in connection therewith in the form of a percentage.

(c)   The Bill of Quantities shall identify work in the Contract to be executed within and below:
(i)   non tidal open water (such as water-courses, streams, rivers, ponds, lakes, canals and the like) at the "open water level" stated in the Contract; or
(ii)   tidal water at the "tide level" stated in the Contract.

The work shall be measured separately, for each Section of the Method of Measurement, and shall be included within the Bill of Quantities under sub headings or in the item description as falling within (i) or (ii) above.

Itemisation—Groups and Features   **3**   Each item description is to be consistent with and be compounded from one or more of the Groups listed under the marginal headings "Itemisation" within the Sections of Part IV of the Method of Measurement incorporating amendments introduced in the Preambles to the Bill of Quantities. An item description may contain Features from as many Groups as necessary to identify the work required, but may include only one Feature from any one Group.

Items in the Bill of Quantities   **4**   The Bill of Quantities, unless expressly stated otherwise in the Contract is to contain all those items compounded in accordance with the foregoing paragraph 3 required to comprise the Works (apart from Provisional Sums and Prime Cost Items which may be required).

Part III

Preparation of Bill of Quantities

Preparation of Bill of Quantities

Subdivision of Bill of Quantities
1 The Bill of Quantities is to be divided as appropriate into separate levels of identification, in the sequence set down in Table 1.
Note. Table 1, level 4 sub headings are advisory.

Quantities
2 Quantities shall be expressed in whole numbers except for units of measurement of tonnes and hectares in which case the quantities shall be to three decimal places.

Units of Measurement
3 The following abbreviations shall be used for the units of measurement:–

Unit	Abbreviation	Unit	Abbreviation
millimetre	mm	sum	sum
metre	m	number	no
square millimetre	mm^2	hour	h
square metre	m^2	week	wk
hectare	ha	item	item
cubic metre	m^3	vehicle week	v/wk
kilogramme	kg	man hour	m/hr
tonne	t	day	day

Special Preliminary Items
4 Provision is made in Table 1 for the inclusion of "Special Preliminary" Items in the Bill of Quantities.

"Special Preliminary" items are not included in Part IV Units and Method of Measurement as their use is intended to be restricted and particular to a given Contract.

"Special Preliminary" items shall not be used for Temporary Works, cofferdams, accesses, advanced operations and the like unless:

The work or operation is unusual in relation to the Works; and

(a) the magnitude of such work, not separately measured, is such as to be disproportionately high in cost in relation to the measured work with which it is associated; or

(b) an operation, not separately measured, is required to be executed far in advance or after the main measured operation to which it relates.

The inclusion of "Special Preliminary" items in a Contract shall be entirely at the discretion of the Engineer. Whether a "Special Preliminary" item is included in the Bill of Quantities or not shall in no way relieve the Contractor of his obligations under the Contract.

Preambles to Bill of Quantities
5 The matters set out under the heading "Preambles to Bill of Quantities" (1-10) hereafter are always to be included as a preamble to the Bill of Quantities. Additional numbered preambles may be included as necessary. Amendments to the Method of Measurement are to be incorporated in the Preambles to Bill of Quantities, (See Part III Amendments to the Method of Measurement and the footnote).

TABLE 1

LEVEL 1 DIVISION	LEVEL 2 CONSTRUCTION HEADING	LEVEL 3 MMHW SECTION HEADINGS	LEVEL 4 SUB HEADINGS	NOTES
(i) Preliminaries	Preliminaries	(1) Preliminaries		Special Preliminaries should be inserted under level 3
(ii) Roadworks	Roadworks General	(2) Site Clearance (3) Hedges Fencing and Noise Barriers (4) Safety Fences (6) Earthworks	Non tidal open water and tidal water	Geotechnics should be inserted under level 4 Hedgebanks and the like should be inserted under Level 3 Section 6
	Main Carriageway	(5) Drainage & Service Ducts (7) Pavements (11) Kerbing, Footways and Paved Areas	Non tidal open water and tidal water	Police Observation Platforms, Cycle tracks, and the like should be inserted under Level 3 Section 11
	Interchanges	(5) Drainage & Service Ducts (7) Pavements (11) Kerbing, Footways and Paved Areas	Non tidal open water and tidal water	Cycle tracks and the like should be inserted under Level 3 Section 11

LEVEL 1 DIVISION	LEVEL 2 CONSTRUCTION HEADING	LEVEL 3 MMHW SECTION HEADINGS	LEVEL 4 SUB HEADINGS	NOTES
	Side Roads	(5) Drainage & Service Ducts (7) Pavements (11) Kerbing, Footways and Paved Areas	Non tidal open water and tidal water	Cycle tracks and the like should be inserted under Level 3 Section 11
	Signs and Lighting	(12) Traffic Signs and Road Markings (13) Road Lighting Columns and Brackets (14) Electrical Work for Road Lighting and Traffic Signs		

DIVISION	SUBDIVISION	LEVEL 2 CONSTRUCTION HEADING	LEVEL 3 MMHW SECTION HEADINGS	LEVEL 4 SUB HEADINGS	NOTES
(11) Structure	Structure in form of Bridge or Viaduct; Name or Reference	Special Preliminaries			Special Preliminaries shall be inserted as a separate construction heading under Level 2
		Piling	(16) Piling and Diaphragm Walling	Non tidal open water and tidal water	

LEVEL 1		LEVEL 2 CONSTRUCTION HEADING	LEVEL 3 MMHW SECTION HEADINGS	LEVEL 4 SUB HEADINGS	NOTES
DIVISION	SUBDIVISION				
		Sub Structure – End Supports	(5) Drainage & Ducts (6) Earthworks (11) Kerbing, Footways and Paved Areas (17) Structural Concrete (18) Steelwork for Structures (19) Protection of Steelwork against Corrosion (23) Bridge Expansion Joints and Sealing of Gaps (24) Brickwork, Blockwork and Stonework	Non tidal open water and tidal water	To include wing walls, and paved areas beneath structures
		Substructure – Intermediate Supports	As for End Supports	As for End Supports	To include Piers and Columns
		Substructure – Main Span			
		Substructure – Approach Spans			

15

LEVEL 1		LEVEL 2 CONSTRUCTION HEADING	LEVEL 3 MMHW SECTION HEADINGS	LEVEL 4 SUB HEADINGS	NOTES
DIVISION	SUBDIVISION				
		Superstructure Superstructure - Main Span Superstructure - Approach Spans Superstructure - Arch Ribs	(5) Drainage & Service Ducts (17) Structural Concrete (18) Steelwork for Structures (19) Protection of Steelwork against Corrosion (21) Bridge Bearings (23) Bridge Expansion Joints and Sealing of Gaps (24) Brickwork, Blockwork and Stonework		
		Finishings	(4) Safety Fences (6) Earthworks (7) Pavements (11) Kerbing, Footways and Paved Areas (20) Waterproofing for Structures (22) Parapets (24) Brickwork, Blockwork and Stonework		Pavements, Footways and the like to be included here if no Roadworks Bill of Quantities.
	Retaining Wall, Subway, Gantry, Culvert, Large Headwall, Corrugated Metal Structure, Gabion Wall, Diaphragm Wall and the like; Name or Reference	Special Preliminaries			Special preliminaries should be inserted as a separate construction heading under Level 2

LEVEL 1		LEVEL 2 CONSTRUCTION HEADING	LEVEL 3 MMHW SECTION HEADINGS	LEVEL 4 SUB HEADINGS	NOTES
DIVISION	SUBDIVISION				
		Main Construction	(5) Drainage & Service Ducts	Non tidal open water and tidal water	Culvert shall exclude piped culverts measured in Section 5 Drainage.
			(6) Earthworks		
			(11) Kerbing, Footways and Paved Areas		
			(16) Piling and Diaphragm Walls		
			(17) Structural Concrete		
			(18) Steelwork for Structures		
			(19) Protection of Steelwork against Corrosion		
			(23) Bridge Expansion Joints and Sealing of Gaps		
			(24) Brickwork, Blockwork and Stonework		
		Finishings	(4) Safety Fences		Pavements, Footways and the like to be included here if no Roadworks Bill of Quantities.
			(6) Earthworks		
			(7) Pavements		
			(11) Kerbing, Footways and Paved Areas		
		Finishings contd	(20) Waterproofing for Structures		
			(22) Parapets		
			(24) Brickwork, Blockwork and Stonework		

17

LEVEL 1 DIVISION	LEVEL 2 CONSTRUCTION HEADING	LEVEL 3 MMHW SECTION HEADINGS	LEVEL 4 SUB HEADINGS	NOTES
(iv) Service Areas	Roadworks Structures	To comply with the principles set down above for Roadworks and Structures	To comply with the principles set down above for Roadworks and Structures	
(v) Maintenance Compounds	Roadworks Structures			
(vi) Accommodation Works	Interest - name or reference			
(vii) Works for Statutory or other Bodies	Body - name or reference			
(viii) Daywork	Daywork			
(ix) PC and Provisional Sum	PC and Provisional Sum			To include PC and Provisional sums not allocated to a particular construction heading.

Preambles to Bill of Quantities

General Directions

1   In this Bill of Quantities the sub-headings and item descriptions identify the work covered by the respective items, read in conjunction with the matters listed against the relevant marginal headings "Item coverage" in Part IV of the Method of Measurement for Highway Works published by Her Majesty's Stationery Office in 1987 and amendments included in these Preambles. The nature and extent of the work is to be ascertained by reference to the Drawings, Specification, Highway Construction Details, and Conditions of Contract. The rates and prices entered in the Bill of Quantities shall be deemed to be the full inclusive value of the work covered by the several items including the following, unless expressly stated otherwise:

(i)   Labour and costs in connection therewith.

(ii)   The supply of materials, goods, storage and costs in connection therewith including delivery to Site. Taking delivery of materials and goods supplied by others, unloading, storage, and costs in connection therewith.

(iii)   Plant and costs in connection therewith.

(iv)   Fixing, erecting and installing or placing of materials and goods in position.

(v)   Temporary Works.

(vi)   The effect on the phasing of the Works of alterations or additions to existing services and supplies to the extent that such work is set forth or reasonably implied in the documents on which the tender is based.

(vii)   General obligations, liabilities and risks involved in the execution of the Works set forth or reasonably implied in the documents on which the tender is based.

(viii)Establishment charges, overheads and profit.

(ix)   Waste.

(x)   Attendance and transport for sampling and testing carried out by the Engineer, and supplying results of tests carried out by the Contractor.

(xi)   Complying with Quality Assurance standards.

(xii)   Preparation and supply of detailed working drawings.

Measurement

2   The measurement of work shall be computed net from the dimensions stated in the Contract unless stated otherwise in the Method of Measurement.

Pricing of Items

3   Each individual item shall have a rate or price entered against it. Rates and prices shall be expressed to two decimal places.

Use of Alternative Specified Materials or Designs

4   Where in the Contract a choice of alternative materials or designs is indicated for a given purpose, the description billed and the rates and prices inserted shall be deemed to cover any of the permitted alternative materials or designs which the Contractor may elect to use. The measurement of all work shall be based upon the thinnest alternative pavement construction and surfacing over structures permitted by the Contract.

Privately and Publicly Owned Services or Supplies

5   The information in the Contract as to the whereabouts of existing services and mains is believed to be correct but the Contractor shall not be relieved of his obligations under the Contract. The Contractor shall include in his rates and prices for locating and taking measures for the support and full protection of pipes, cables and other apparatus during the progress of the Works obtaining the written consent of the appropriate authority to interrupt the service or supply and for keeping the Engineer informed of all arrangements he makes with the owners of privately owned services or supplies, Statutory Undertakers and Public Authorities as appropriate.

Labours

6 Labours in connection with nominated Sub-Contractors shall include:

(a) in the case of work or services executed, for affording the use of existing working space, access, temporary roads, erected scaffolding, working shelters, staging, ladders, hoists, storage, latrines, messing, welfare and other facilities existing on Site and the provision of protection, water, electricity for lighting and clearing away rubbish and debris arising from the work;

(b) in the case of goods, materials or services supplied, for taking delivery, unloading, storing, protecting and returning crates, cartons and packing materials.

Roadworks Overall Requirements

7 The Contractor shall allow in his rates and prices for complying with requirements in respect of Pavement Construction, Horizontal Alignments, Surface Levels and Surface Regularity of Pavement Courses, Cold Weather Working, Use of Surfaces by Traffic and Construction Plant, and General Requirements for Sub-Bases and Road Bases.

Work Within and Below Non-Tidal Open Water or Tidal Water

8 The Contractor shall allow in his rates and prices for taking measures required to execute the work separately measured as being within and below non-tidal open water or tidal water. For the measurement of work affected by non-tidal open water or tidal water the datum stated in the Contract shall be used irrespective of the actual level of water encountered in the Works.

Dealing with Flow

9 The Contractor shall allow in his rates and prices for taking measures to deal with the existing flow of water, sewage and the like.

Reimbursement by the Employer of Fees, Rates, Taxes and Engineers Telephone Calls

10 The Employer will reimburse the Contractor the actual price paid by the Contractor in respect of:

(i) fees, rates and taxes—the sums certified by the Engineer as properly repayable to the Contractor in accordance with Clause 26 of the Conditions of Contract;

(ii) engineers telephone calls—telephone calls charged to the number or numbers allocated to the Engineer.

Any other cost, charge or expense in respect of these items shall be allowed for in the rates and prices for temporary accommodation.

*Amendment to the Method of Measurement

For the purpose of this Contract the Method of Measurement referred to in Preamble 1 General Directions is amended in accordance with the pages immediately following.

*Footnote

Where amendments to Part IV of the Method of Measurement are required in accordance with paragraph 1(b) of General Principles, this preamble should be the last numbered preamble and inserted immediately prior to the amendments.

Part IV

Units and Methods of Measurement

Section 1: Preliminaries

Definition

1 The definition of:

(a) "Until completion of the Works" shall mean until completion of the whole of the Works certified by the Engineer in accordance with Clause 48(1) of the Conditions of Contract;

(b) "After completion of the Works" shall mean subsequent to (a) defined above either until the issue of the Maintenance Certificate in accordance with Clause 61(1) of the Conditions of Contract, or for such lesser period specified in the Contract.

Temporary Accommodation

Units

2 The units of measurement shall be:

(i) erection, servicing, dismantling of temporary accommodation ....item.

Itemisation

3 Separate items shall be provided for temporary accommodation in accordance with Part II paragraphs 3 and 4 and the following:

Group	Feature	
I	1	Erection.
	2	Servicing.
	3	Dismantling.
II	1	Principal offices for the Engineer.
	2	Principal laboratories for the Engineer.
	3	Portable offices for the Engineer.
	4	Portable laboratories for the Engineer.
	5	Offices and messes for the Contractor.
	6	Stores and workshops for the Contractor.
III	1	Provided by the Employer.
IV	1	At the place of fabrication or manufacture.
V	1	Until completion of the Works.
	2	After completion of the Works.

Erection of Temporary Accommodation

4 The items for erection of temporary accommodation shall in accordance with the Preambles to Bill of Quantities General Directions include for:

Item coverage

(i) in the case of accommodation for the Contractor,

    (a) everything required by the Contractor.

(ii) in the case of accommodation for the Engineer,

    (a) initial accommodation and equipment, maintenance, servicing and removing;

    (b) sites for the accommodation;

    (c) preparation of sites;

    (d) foundations, bases and hardstandings;

    (e) water, sanitation, heating, power and lighting services;

    (f) fences, notice and direction boards;

    (g) vehicle access, hardstandings, parking areas and footpaths;

    (h) equipment, furnishings, fittings, supplies and initial consumable stores;

    (i) telephones, extensions, switchboard and switching systems separately connected to the telephone system.

(iii) in the case of accommodation for the Engineer provided by the Employer,

    (a) as paragraph 4(ii)(a) to (i) of this section;

    (b) alterations and refurbishments;

Servicing Temporary Accommodation

Item coverage

5 The items for servicing temporary accommodation shall in accordance with the Preambles to Bill of Quantities General Directions include for:

(i) in the case of accommodation for the Contractor,

    (a) everything required by the Contractor.

(ii) in the case of accommodation for the Engineer,

    (a) rental and leasing including telephone rental;

    (b) heating, sanitation, power, lighting and water;

    (c) depreciation and maintenance of buildings, services, fences, notice and direction boards, vehicle access, parking areas, hardstandings and footpaths;

    (d) depreciation, maintenance and replacement of equipment, furnishings, fittings and supplies;

    (e) cleaning accommodation;

    (f) moving and re-establishing portable accommodation as required;

    (g) replenishment of consumable stores;

    (h) repairing, replacing, calibration of equipment;

    (i) disposal of waste.

Dismantling Temporary Accommodation

Item coverage

6 The items for dismantling temporary accommodation shall in accordance with the Preambles to Bill of Quantities General Directions include for:

(a) receiving back from the Engineer and removing equipment, furniture, fittings and supplies off Site;

(b) disconnecting, removing and sealing off disused services;

(c) demolishing and removing off Site temporary accommodation, vehicle access, hardstanding, parking areas, footpaths, fences, notice and direction boards;

(d) disposal of material (as Section 6 paragraph 32);

(e) reinstatement of the sites occupied by temporary accommodation;

(f) in the case of accommodation for the Engineer, the credit value of surplus equipment or material which becomes the property of the Contractor and transport and delivery to the Employer of equipment or material which becomes the property of the Employer;

(g) in the case of accommodation for the Engineer provided by the Employer, handing back to the Employer in the condition specified.

Vehicles for the Engineer

Units

7 The units of measurement shall be:

(i) vehicles for the Engineer .... vehicle week.

Measurement

8 The measurement of vehicles for the Engineer shall be each week or part thereof during which a vehicle is provided.

Itemisation

9 Separate items shall be provided for vehicles for the Engineer in accordance with Part II paragraphs 3 and 4 and the following:

Group		Feature
I	1	Each type of vehicle for the Engineer.
II	1	Until completion of the Works.
	2	After completion of the Works.

Vehicles for the Engineer

10 The items for vehicles for the Engineer shall in accordance with the Preamble to Bill of Quantities General Directions include for:

Item coverage

(a) equipment;

(b) taxing for use on public highways and for the carriage of goods and samples;

(c) comprehensive insurance;

(d) suitable replacement including equipment;

(e) depreciation;

(f) maintenance in a roadworthy condition and in conformity with the vehicle manufacturer's recommendations;

(g) fuel and oil;

(h) keeping clean inside and out;

(i) collection from Site when the vehicle is returned.

Radio Communication system for the Engineer

Units

11 The units of measurement shall be:

(i) radio communication system for the Engineer .... item.

Itemisation

12 Separate items shall be provided for radio communication system for the Engineer in accordance with Part II paragraphs 3 and 4 and the following:

Group		Feature
I	1	Radio communication system for the Engineer.
II	1	Until completion of the Works.
	2	After completion of the Works.

Radio Communication System for the Engineer

13 The items for radio communication system for the Engineer shall in accordance with the Preambles to Bill of Quantities General Directions include for:

Item coverage

(a) confirming licences, wavelengths and channels with the Department of Trade and Industry and costs arising therefrom;

(b) equipment and installation;

(c) rental, running costs and power;

(d) depreciation, maintenance and repairs;

(e) replacement equipment;

(f) receiving back from Engineer and removing equipment and supplies off Site.

Operatives for the Engineer

Units

14 The units of measurement shall be:

(i) operatives for the Engineer .... day.

Measurement

15 The measurement of operatives for the Engineer shall be a continuous period of four hours or more within any one day during which the operatives services are supplied in accordance with the written order of the Engineer.

Itemisation

16 Separate items shall be provided for operatives for the Engineer in accordance with Part II paragraphs 3 and 4 and the following:

Group	Feature	
I	1	Each type of operative for the Engineer.
II	1	Until completion of the Works.
	2	After completion of the Works.

Operatives for the Engineer

Item coverage

17 The items for operatives for the Engineer shall in accordance with the Preambles to Bill of Quantities General Directions include for:

(a) the wages and other emoluments paid including payment for overtime;

(b) working outside the Contractor's normal working hours if so required by the Engineer;

(c) costs and expenses incurred consequent upon the employment or hiring;

(d) periods of less than four hours.

Information Board

Units

18 The units of measurement shall be:

(i) information board .... number.

Itemisation

19 Separate items shall be provided for information boards in accordance with Part II paragraphs 3 and 4 and the following:

Group	Feature	
I	1	Information board.
II	1	Different types.

Information board

Item coverage

20 The items for information board shall in accordance with the Preambles to Bill of Quantities General Directions include for:

(a) excavation of acceptable material (as Section 6 paragraphs 16 and 17);

(b) excavation of unacceptable material (as Section 6 paragraph 18);

(c) excavation of hard material (as Section 6 paragraph 22);

(d) backfilling and compaction;

(e) in-situ concrete (as Section 17 paragraph 4);

(f) formwork (as Section 17 paragraph 14);

(g) disposal of material (as Section 6 paragraph 32);

(h) painting, reflectorisation and illumination;

(i) cleaning, maintaining and repairing;

(j) dismantling and removing from Site;

(k) unless otherwise stated in the Contract, reinstatement of surfaces.

Temporary Diversion for Traffic

Units

21 The units of measurement shall be:

(i) taking measures for or construction, maintenance, removal of temporary diversion for traffic .... item.

Itemisation

22 Separate items shall be provided for temporary diversion for traffic in accordance with Part II paragraphs 3 and 4 and the following:

Group		Feature
I	1	Taking measures for or construction of temporary diversion for traffic.
	2	Maintenance of measures for or construction of temporary diversion for traffic.
	3	Removal of measures for or construction of temporary diversion for traffic.
II	1	At locations listed in the Appendix.
	2	At those locations listed in the Appendix but not measured individually.

Taking Measures for or Construction of Temporary Diversion for Traffic

23 The items for taking measures for or construction of temporary diversion for traffic shall in accordance with the Preambles to Bill of Quantities General Directions include for:

Item coverage

(a) obtaining licences and agreements;

(b) making arrangements with owners and occupiers of land temporarily required and costs arising therefrom;

(c) preparing, amending and submitting to the Engineer and other interested bodies, proposals and programme;

(d) consulting with Police and other authorities;

(e) preparation of site;

(f) site clearance, fencing, drainage, earthworks, pavements, kerbing, footways, traffic signs, road markings, road lighting, structures, parapets, ramps and accesses;

(g) temporary diversion of services.

Maintenance of Measures for or Construction of Temporary Diversions for Traffic

24 The items for maintenance of measures for or construction of temporary diversions for traffic shall in accordance with the Preambles to the Bill of Quantities General Directions provide for:–

Item coverage

(a) continuous adequate provision for traffic flows;

(b) modifications.

Removal of Measures for or Construction of Temporary Diversions for Traffic

25 The items for removal of measures for or construction of temporary diversions for traffic shall in accordance with the Preambles to the Bill of Quantities General Directions include for:

Item coverage

(a) breaking up diversion;

(b) disposal of material (as Section 6 paragraph 32);

(c) unless otherwise stated in the Contract, reinstatement of the site to its previous condition.

Traffic Safety and Management

Units

26 The units of measurement shall be:

(i) Traffic Safety and Management .... item.

Itemisation

27 Separate items shall be provided for traffic safety and management in accordance with Part II paragraphs 3 and 4 and the following:

Group		Feature
I	1	Traffic Safety and Management.

Traffic Safety and Management

Item coverage

28 The items for traffic safety and management shall in accordance with the Preambles to the Bill of Quantity General Direction include for:

(a) complying with the recommendations contained in Chapter 8 of the "Traffic Signs Manual" published by Her Majesty's Stationery Office and any amendment thereto or where the circumstances of any particular case are not covered submitting proposals for dealing with such situations to the Engineer for his consent;

(b) complying with particular requirements of the Contract;

(c) consulting with statutory, Police or other authorities concerned, submitting to the Engineer for his consent, proposals based on such consultation showing a scheme of traffic safety and management measures including details of Emergency Routes and furnishing such details as necessitated by the Works or as the Engineer may require;

(d) awaiting Engineer's consent to proposals;

(e) traffic signs, road markings, lamps, barriers, and traffic control signals including maintaining, cleaning, repositioning, covering, uncovering and removing;

(f) complying with the requirements for labour and plant working on or adjacent to a trafficked highway, at entry and exit points to the Site including signing;

(g) road lighting, modification, and removal;

(h) giving of notice to the Engineer;

Progress Photographs

Units

29 The units of measurement shall be:

(i) set of progress photographs, set of aerial progress photographs.................number.

(ii) additional progress photographs, additional aerial progress photographs-.................number.

Measurement

30 A set of photographs shall comprise such numbers of negatives and prints as described in the Contract taken on any one flight or visit to Site.

Where in any one flight or visit the Engineer orders less than one complete set of photographs, then one set shall be measured.

Where in any flight or visit the Engineer orders progress or aerial photographs in excess of the number in the set then the additional photographs shall be measured and be deemed to include the negative and the same number of prints per negative as those in the set.

Itemisation

31 Separate items shall be provided for progress photographs in accordance with Part II paragraphs 3 and 4 and the following:

Group	Feature
I	1 Set of progress photographs. 2 Set of aerial progress photographs. 3 Additional progress photographs. 4 Additional aerial progress photographs.
II	1 Monochrome prints. 2 Colour prints.

Progress Photographs, Aerial Progress Photographs, Additional Progress Photographs, Additional Aerial Progress Photographs

32 The items for progress photographs, aerial progress photographs, additional progress photographs and additional aerial progress photographs shall in accordance with the Preambles to Bill of Quantities General Directions include for:

Item coverage

(a) delivery of negatives and prints to the Engineer;

(b) identification marking on the prints;

(c) albums.

Recovery Vehicles

Units

33 The units of measurement shall be:

(i) Recovery vehicle .... item.

34 Separate items shall be provided for recovery vehicles in accordance with Part II paragraphs 3 and 4 and the following:

Group	Feature
I	1 Each type of recovery vehicle.

Recovery Vehicles

Item coverage

35 The items for recovery vehicles shall in accordance with the Preambles to Bill of Quantities General Directions include for:

(a) equipment including radio equipment;

(b) taxing for use on public highways;

(c) comprehensive insurance;

(d) replacement vehicle including equipment;

(e) depreciation;

(f) maintenance;

(g) fuel, oil and other consumables;

(h) AVRO qualified operatives;

(i) completion and submission of log sheets;

(j) dealing with shed loads, broken down, accident damaged or abandoned vehicles and removal;

(k) explanatory leaflets and distribution;

(l) liaising with Police;

(m) hardstandings, accommodation and servicing;

(n) removal;

(o) membership of AVRO.

Section 2: Site Clearance

1 Unless otherwise stated in the Contract the items in this Section shall include for the removal of superficial obstructions down to existing ground level. With the exception of items measured under paragraph 7 and those including for the removal of stumps and roots, work below existing ground level in the demolition and removal of foundations, chambers, cellars, ground slabs, carriageways, kerbs, pavings, backfilling and the like shall be measured in Section 6 Earthworks.

Site Clearance

Units

2 The units of measurement shall be:

(i) general site clearance ....hectare.

(ii) demolition of individual or groups of buildings or structures ....item.

Measurement

3 The measurement of general site clearance shall be the plan area. No deduction shall be made for buildings, structures carriageways and the like.

Itemisation

4 Separate items shall be provided for site clearance in accordance with Part II paragraphs 3 and 4 and the following:

Group	Feature	
I	1	General site clearance.
	2	General site clearance of separate sections.
	3	Demolition of individual or groups of buildings or structures.

General Site Clearance

5 The items for general site clearance shall in accordance with the Preambles to Bill of Quantities General Directions include for:

Item coverage

(a) demolition, breaking up and removal;

(b) tree felling;

(c) grubbing up and blasting stumps and roots;

(d) uprooting of bushes, small trees and hedges;

(e) credit value of materials;

(f) disposal of material (as Section 6 paragraph 32);

(g) making good severed ends of existing fences, hedges and walls;

(h) branch lopping and treatment;

(i) disconnecting removing and sealing services and supplies.

Demolition of Individual or Groups of Buildings or Structures

6 The items for demolition of individual or groups of buildings or structures shall in accordance with the Preamble to Bill of Quantities General Directions include for:

Item coverage

(a) blasting, breaking up and removal;

(b) credit value of materials;

(c) disposal of material (as Section 6 paragraph 32);

(d) disconnecting, removing and sealing services and supplies.

Take Up or Down and Set Aside for Reuse or Remove to Store off Site

Units

7 The units of measurement shall be:
Take up or down and set aside for reuse or remove to store off Site the following:

(i) paved areas and the like...............square metre.

(ii) kerbing, channelling, edging, fencing, safety fences and the like .... linear metre.

(iii) road lighting columns, brackets and wall mountings, traffic signs, roadstuds, gates, street furniture and the like ....number.

(iv) chamber covers and frames, gully gratings and frames and the like ....
number.

Measurement

8 The measurement for take up or down and set aside for reuse or remove to store off site paved areas and the like and kerbing, channelling, edging, fencing, safety fences and the like shall be the areas and lengths stated in the Contract.

Itemisation

9 Separate items shall be provided for take up or down and set aside for reuse or remove to store off Site in accordance with Part II paragraphs 3 and 4 and the following:

Group	Feature
I	1 Take up or down and set aside for reuse.
	2 Take up or down and remove to store off Site.
II	1 Paved areas and the like.
	2 Kerbing, channelling, edging, fencing, safety fences and the like.
	3 Road lighting columns brackets and wall mountings, traffic signs, gates, street furniture, road studs and the like.
	4 Chamber covers and frames, gully gratings and frames and the like.
III	1 Different types and sizes.

Take up or Down and Set Aside for Reuse or remove to store off Site

10 The items for take up or down and set aside for reuse or remove to store off Site shall in accordance with the Preamble to Bill of Quantities General Directions include for:

Item coverage

(a) excavation of acceptable material (as Section 6 paragraphs 16 and 17);

(b) excavation of unacceptable material (as Section 6 paragraph 18);

(c) excavation of hard material (as Section 6 paragraph 22);

(d) breaking up foundations;

(e) dismantling;

(f) cleaning, stacking, protecting and labelling;

(g) transport and handling;

(h) disconnecting removing and sealing of services and supplies;

(i) backfilling and compaction.

(j) making good to severed ends of existing walls, hedges, and fencing;

(k) disposal of material (as Section 6 paragraph 32);

(l) reinstatement and making good;

(m) storage facilities;

(n) in the case of removal of safety fences, dismantling of beams, breaking up footings, extracting posts, cleaning, protecting, labelling and transporting beams and posts to store off Site;

(o) replacing items damaged during the foregoing operations.

Section 3: Hedges, Fencing and Noise Barriers

Hedges

Units

1 The units of measurement shall be:

(i) hedges ....linear metre.

Measurement

2 The measurement of hedges shall be the developed length along the centre line of the hedge.

Itemisation

3 Separate items shall be provided for hedges in accordance with Part II paragraphs 3 and 4 and the following:

Group	Feature
I	1 Each species of hedge.
II	1 Different spacings of plants.
III	1 Hedges with protective fencing.

Hedges

Item coverage

4 The items for hedges shall in accordance with the Preambles to Bill of Quantities General Directions include for:

(a) excavation of acceptable material (as Section 6 Paragraphs 16 and 17);

(b) excavation of unacceptable material (as Section 6 Paragraph 18);

(c) excavation of hard material (as Section 6 Paragraph 22);

(d) filling of trench with topsoil from any source;

(e) cultivating and planting;

(f) protection of plants from injurious weather;

(g) fertilising, watering and weeding;

(h) maintenance and replacement;

(i) disposal of material (as Section 6 Paragraph 32);

(j) fencing (as this Section Paragraph 8).

Fencing, Gates and Stiles

Units

5 The units of measurement shall be:

(i) fencing, ...linear metre.

(ii) concrete footing to intermediate posts .... number.

(iii) gates, stiles, ... number.

Measurement

6 Temporary fencing required by the Contractor in the discharge of his obligations under Clauses 19 and 22 of the Conditions of Contract shall not be measured.

The measurement of fencing shall be the developed length along the centre line of the fence. The measurement of height of fencing shall be that stated in the Contract for the type of fence.

The measurement of width of gates shall be the distance between the outer edges of the stiles, the outer edges of hanging stiles in the case of double gates.

The measurement of heights of gates shall be the distance between the upper surface of the top rail and the underside of the bottom rail.

Concrete footing to intermediate posts shall only be measured for those locations stated in the Contract.

Itemisation

7 Separate items shall be provided for fencing in accordance with Part II paragraphs 3 and 4 and the following:

Group	Feature
I	1 Each type of fencing.
	2 Concrete footing to intermediate posts of each type of fencing.
	3 Each type of gate.
	4 Each type of stile.
II	1 Fencing of different heights.
	2 Gates of different heights and widths.
III	1 Painted fencing, gates or stiles.

Fencing

8 The items for fencing shall in accordance with the Preambles to Bill of Quantities General Directions include for:

Item coverage

(a) excavation of acceptable material (as Section 6 Paragraphs 16 and 17);

(b) excavation of unacceptable material (as Section 6 Paragraph 18);

(c) excavation of hard material (as Section 6 paragraph 22);

(d) trimming ground on the line of the fencing;

(e) in situ concrete (as Section 17 paragraph 4);

(f) formwork (as Section 17 paragraph 14);

(g) reinforcement (as Section 17 paragraph 25);

(h) backfilling and compaction;

(i) disposal of material (as Section 6 paragraph 32);

(j) preservation of timber;

(k) adjustment of fencing to a flowing alignment including additional length posts;

(l) fittings;

(m) joining to existing fencing, gates, hedges and walls;

(n) protective system (as Section 19 paragraph 4);

(o) inspection and maintenance of fencing and gates;

(p) erection and removal of temporary fencing and gates;

(q) additional posts and rails over ditches;

(r) maintenance of access for owners, tenants and occupiers of adjoining land and patrolling gaps or openings;

(s) epoxy resin compound and mastic filler to posts fixed in sockets.

Concrete Footing to Intermediate Posts

Item coverage

9 The items for concrete footing to intermediate posts shall in accordance with the Preambles to Bill of Quantities General Directions include for:

(a) excavation of acceptable material (as Section 6 Paragraphs 16 and 17);

(b) excavation of unacceptable material (as Section 6 Paragraph 18);

(c) excavation of hard material (as Section 6 paragraph 22);

(d) in situ concrete (as Section 17 paragraph 4);

(e) formwork (as Section 17 paragraph 14);

(f) reinforcement (as Section 17 paragraph 25);

(g) backfilling and compaction;

(h) disposal of material (as Section 6 paragraph 32).

Gates and Stiles

Item coverage

10 The items for gates and stiles shall in accordance with the Preambles to Bill of Quantities General Directions include for:

(a) excavation of acceptable material (as Section 6 Paragraphs 16 and 17);

(b) excavation of unacceptable material (as Section 6 Paragraph 18);

(c) excavation of hard material (as Section 6 paragraph 22);

(d) trimming ground at entrance;

(e) in situ concrete (as Section 17 paragraph 4);

(f) formwork (as Section 17 paragraph 14);

(g) reinforcement (as Section 17 paragraph 25);

(h) backfilling and compaction;

(i) disposal of material (as Section 6 paragraph 32);

(j) preservation of timber;

(k) protective system (as Section 19 paragraph 4);

(l) posts, fittings and furniture;

(m) joining to existing fencing, hedges and walls;

(n) in the case of new gates and stiles in existing fencing, hedges or walls, forming openings and making good.

Remove from Store and Re-erect Fencing, Gates and Stiles.

Units

11 The units of measurement shall be:

(i) remove from store and re-erect fencing .... linear metre;

(ii) concrete footing to intermediate posts .... number;

(iii) remove from store and re-erect gates and stiles .... number.

Measurement

12 The measurement of re-erected fencing shall be the developed length along the centre line of the re-erected fencing. The measurement of height of fencing shall be that stated in the Contract for the type of fence.

The measurement of width of gates shall be the distance between the outer edges of the stiles, the outer edges of hanging stiles in the case of double gates.

The measurement of heights of gates shall be the distance between the upper surface of the top rail and the underside of the bottom rail.

Concrete footing to intermediate posts shall only be measured for those locations stated in the Contract.

Itemisation

13 Separate items shall be provided for re-erected fencing, gates and stiles in accordance with Part II paragraphs 3 and 4 and the following:

Group	Feature	
I	1	Each type of re-erected fencing.
	2	Concrete footing to intermediate posts of each type of re-erected fencing.
	3	Each type of re-erected gate.
	4	Each type of re-erected stile.
II	1	Re-erected fencing of different heights.
	2	Re-erected gates of different heights and widths.
III	1	Re-erected painted fencing, gates or stiles.

Remove from Store and Re-erect Fencing

14 The items for remove from store and re-erect fencing shall in accordance with the Preambles to Bill of Quantities General Directions include for:

Item coverage

(a) loading, transporting from store, unloading and positioning for re-erection;

(b) replacing items damaged during the foregoing operations;

(c) modification and new materials;

(d) painting existing painted items;

(e) fencing (as this Section Paragraph 8).

Concrete Footing to Intermediate Posts

15 The items for concrete footing to intermediate posts shall in accordance with the Preambles to Bill of Quantities General Directions include for:

Item coverage

(a) Concrete footings to intermediate posts (as this Section Paragraph 9).

Remove from Store and Re-erect Gates and Stiles

16 The items for remove from store and re-erect gates and stiles shall in accordance with the Preambles to Bill of Quantities General Directions include for:

Item coverage

(a) loading, transporting from store, unloading and positioning for re-erection;

(b) replacing items damaged during the foregoing operations;

(c) modification and new materials;

(d) painting existing painted items;

(e) gates and stiles (as this Section Paragraph 10);

Walls

Units
Measurement
Itemisation

17 Walls and the like shall be measured in accordance with the units of measurement, measurement and itemisation set out in the relevant Sections of the Method of Measurement.

Pedestrian Guard Rails and Handrails

Units

18 The units of measurement shall be:

(i) pedestrian guard rails, handrails .... linear metre.

Measurement **19** The measurement of pedestrian guard rails and handrails shall be the developed length along the centre line. The height of pedestrian guard rails shall be the height between the top of the top rail and the finished surface level to which the posts are attached to or inserted into.

Itemisation **20** Separate items shall be provided for pedestrian guard rails and handrails in accordance with Part II paragraphs 3 and 4 and the following:

Group		Feature
I	1	Each type of pedestrian guard rail.
	2	Each type of handrail.
II	1	Different heights.

Pedestrian Guard Rails and Handrails

21 The items for pedestrian guard rails and handrails shall in accordance with the Preambles to Bill of Quantities General Directions include for:

Item coverage

(a) excavation of acceptable material (as Section 6 Paragraphs 16 and 17);

(b) excavation of unacceptable material (as Section 6 Paragraph 18);

(c) excavation of hard material (as Section 6 Paragraph 22);

(d) in situ concrete (as Section 17 Paragraph 4);

(e) formwork (as Section 17 Paragraph 14);

(f) reinforcement (as Section 17 Paragraph 25);

(g) backfilling and compaction;

(h) disposal of material (as Section 6 paragraph 32);

(i) metal parapets (as Section 22 paragraph 4);

(j) gates.

Noise Barriers

Units **22** The units of measurement shall be:

(i) noise barriers .... linear metre.

Measurement **23** The measurement shall be the developed length along the centre line of the noise barrier.
The measurement of height of noise barrier shall be that stated in the Contract for the type of noise barrier.

Itemisation **24** Separate items shall be provided for noise barriers in accordance with Part II paragraphs 3 and 4 and the following:

Group		Feature
I	1	Each type of noise barrier.
II	1	Noise barriers of different heights.

Noise Barriers

25 The items for noise barriers shall in accordance with the Preambles to Bill of Quantities General Directions include for:

Item coverage

(a) excavation of acceptable material (as Section 6 Paragraphs 16 and 17);

(b) excavation of unacceptable material (as Section 6 Paragraph 18);

(c) excavation of hard material (as Section 6 Paragraph 22);

(d) trimming ground on the line of the noise barrier;

(e) in situ concrete (as Section 17 Paragraph 4);

(f) formwork (as Section 17 Paragraph 14);

(g) reinforcement (as Section 17 Paragraph 25);

(h) backfilling and compaction;

(i) disposal of material (as Section 6 paragraph 32);

(j) preservation of timber;

(k) burying the bottom of the noise barrier or gravel board;

(l) sample panels;

(m) gates and fittings;

(n) adjustment of noise barrier to a flowing alignment;

(o) protective system (as Section 19 paragraph 4);

(p) in the case of integrated safety fence forming pockets and casting in sockets;

(q) supply of design certificates;

(r) awaiting Engineer's approval of sample panels;

(s) fixing to structures.

Section 4: Safety Fences

Definition

1   The term "beam" shall mean a longitudinal member spanning posts and mounting brackets within the limits defined in paragraph 3 below and shall be deemed to include the terms "barrier", "rail", "safety fence", and "guardrail" for vehicles. The term "mounting bracket" shall be deemed to include the term "bridge pier or concrete parapet mounting connection".

Safety Fences

Units

2   The units of measurement shall be:

(i)   beams .... linear metre.

(ii)   posts, mounting brackets, terminals, full height anchorages, expansion joint anchorages, connections to bridge parapets, transition pieces, concrete footing to posts .... number.

Measurement

3   The measurement of beams shall be the developed length along the centre line of the beams or in the case of double sided fences, measured once only along the centre line of the posts between the following points:

(a)   the end of each beam type at a connection to bridge parapet or within a transition piece assembly;

(b)   the connection of beams to terminals, full height anchorages and expansion joint anchorages.

4   The measurement of terminals, full height anchorages, expansion joint anchorages and connections to bridge parapets shall be the complete installation including posts and concrete. Mounting brackets and all other posts required between those points defined in paragraph 3 shall be measured and concrete footing to those posts shall only be measured where no other alternative method of fixing is permitted.

5   The measurement of transition pieces shall be the complete installation.

Itemisation

6   Separate items shall be provided for safety fences in accordance with Part II paragraphs 3 and 4 and the following:

Group	Feature	
I	1	Each type of beam.
	2	Each type of post.
	3	Each type of mounting bracket.
	4	Each type of terminal.
	5	Each type of full height anchorage.
	6	Each type of expansion joint anchorage.
	7	Each type of connection to bridge parapet.
	8	Each type of transition piece.
	9	Each type of concrete footing to post.
II	1	Straight or curved exceeding 50 metres radius.
	2	Curved not exceeding 50 metres radius.

Beams

Item coverage

7 The items for beams shall in accordance with the Preambles to Bill of Quantities General Directions include for:

(a) fabrication and preparation;

(b) protective system (as Section 19 paragraph 4);

(c) attachments, fixings, closure pieces and stiffeners;

(d) adjustment of beams to flowing alignment;

(e) tensioning and flaring;

(f) painting chevrons including background.

Posts

Item coverage

8 The items for posts shall in accordance with the Preambles to Bill of Quantities General Directions include for:

(a) fabrication and preparation;

(b) protective system (as Section 19 paragraph 4);

(c) preservation of timber;

(d) driving or excavation in any material (as Section 6 paragraphs 16, 17, 18 and 22);

(e) backfilling and compaction;

(f) disposal of material (as Section 6 paragraph 32);

(g) concrete footing to posts (as this Section paragraph 11) in lieu of driven post where adopted as a fixing by the Contractor;

(h) fixing to structures;

(i) fixing to beam including spacers.

Mounting Brackets

Item coverage

9 The items for mounting brackets shall in accordance with the Preambles to Bill of Quantities General Directions include for:

(a) fabrication and preparation;

(b) protective system (as Section 19 paragraph 4);

(c) fixing to structures including adaptor platforms;

(d) fixing to beam.

Terminal, Full Height Anchorage, Expansion Joint Anchorage, Connection to Bridge Parapet and Transition Piece

Item coverage

10 The items for terminal, full height anchorage, expansion joint anchorage, connection to bridge parapet and transition piece shall in accordance with the Preambles to Bill of Quantities General Directions include for:

(a) fabrication and preparation;

(b) protective system (as Section 19 paragraph 4);

(c) preservation of timber;

(d) driving or excavation in any material (as Section 6 paragraphs 16, 17, 18 and 22);

(e) in situ concrete (as Section 17 paragraph 4);

(f) formwork (as Section 17 paragraph 14);

(g) reinforcement (as Section 17 paragraph 25);

(h) disposal of material (as Section 6 paragraph 32);

(i) fixing to or setting in concrete;

(j) attachments, fixings and stiffeners;

(k) adjustment to flowing alignment;

(l) tensioning and flaring;

(m) fixing to structures;

(n) terminal end shoes;

(o) fixing to beam;

(p) in the case of terminals to untensioned corrugated beam, acceptable material, ramp, backfilling and compaction;

Concrete Footing to Posts

11 The items for concrete footing to posts shall in accordance with the Preambles to Bill of Quantities General Directions include for:

Item coverage

(a) excavation of acceptable material (as Section 6 paragraphs 16 and 17);

(b) excavation of unacceptable material (as Section 6 paragraph 18);

(c) excavation of hard material (as Section 6 paragraph 22);

(d) in situ concrete (as Section 17 paragraph 4);

(e) formwork (as Section 17 paragraph 14);

(f) reinforcement (as Section 17 paragraph 25);

(h) disposal of material (as Section 6 paragraph 32).

Remove from Store and Re-erect Safety Fences

Units

12 The units of measurement shall be:

(i) remove from store and re-erect beams .... linear metre.

(ii) remove from store and re-erect posts, mounting brackets, terminals, full height anchorages, expansion joint anchorages, connections to bridge parapets, transition pieces, concrete footing to posts .... number.

Measurement

13 The measurement of re-erected safety fences shall be in accordance with paragraphs 3, 4 and 5 of this Section.

Itemisation

14 Separate items shall be provided for remove from store and re-erect safety fences in accordance with Part II paragraphs 3 and 4 and the following:

Group	Feature	
I	1	Each type of re-erected beam.
	2	Each type of re-erected post.
	3	Each type of re-erected mounting bracket.
	4	Each type of re-erected terminal.
	5	Each type of re-erected full height anchorage.
	6	Each type of re-erected expansion joint anchorage.
	7	Each type of re-erected connection to bridge parapet.
	8	Each type of re-erected transition piece.
	9	Each type of concrete footing to re-erected post.
II	1	Straight or curved exceeding 50 metres radius.
	2	Curved not exceeding 50 metres radius.

Remove from Store and Re-erect Beams

15 The items for remove from store and re-erect beams shall in accordance with the Preambles to Bill of Quantities General Directions include for:

Item coverage

(a) loading, transporting from store, unloading and positioning for re-erection;

(b) replacing items damaged during the foregoing operations;

(c) modification and new materials;

(d) beams (as this Section paragraph 7).

Remove from Store and Re-erect Posts

16 The items for remove from store and re-erect posts shall in accordance with the Preambles to Bill of Quantities General Directions include for:

Item coverage

(a) loading, transporting from store, unloading and positioning for re-erection;
(b) replacing items damaged during the foregoing operations;
(c) modification and new materials;
(d) posts (as this Section paragraph 8).

Remove from Store and Re-erect Mounting Brackets

17 The items for remove from store and re-erect mounting brackets shall in accordance with the Preambles to Bill of Quantities General Directions include for:

Item coverage

(a) loading, transporting from store, unloading and positioning for re-erection;
(b) replacing items damaged during the foregoing operations;
(c) modification and new materials;
(d) mounting bracket (as this Section paragraph 9).

Remove from Store and Re-erect Terminal, Full Height Anchorage, Expansion Joint Anchorage, Connection to Bridge Parapet and Transition Piece

18 The items for remove from store and re-erect terminal, full height anchorage, expansion joint anchorage, connection to bridge parapet and transition piece shall in accordance with the Preambles to Bill of Quantities General Directions include for:

Item coverage

(a) loading, transporting from store, unloading and positioning for re-erection;
(b) replacing items damaged during the foregoing operations;
(c) modification and new materials;
(d) terminal, full height anchorage, expansion joint anchorage, connection to bridge parapet and transition piece (as this Section paragraph 10).

Concrete Footing to Re-erected Posts

19 The items for concrete footing to re-erected posts shall in accordance with the Preambles to Bill of Quantities General Directions include for:

Item coverage

(a) concrete footing to posts (as this Section paragraph 11).

Post Extension Unit

Units

20 The unit of measurement shall be:
(i) post extension unit .... number.

Itemisation

21 Separate items shall be provided for post extension unit in accordance with Part II paragraphs 3 and 4 and the following:

Group	Feature
I	1 Post extension unit.

Post Extension Unit

Item coverage

22 The items for post extension unit shall in accordance with the Preamble to the Bill of Quantities General Directions include for:

(a) fabrication and preparation;

(b) protective system (as Section 19 paragraph 4);

(c) drilling existing posts;

(d) fixing to existing posts.

Raising Existing Sockets

Units

23 The unit of measurement shall be:

(i) raising existing socket .... number.

Itemisation

24 Separate items shall be provided for raising existing socket in accordance with Part II paragraphs 3 and 4 and the following:

Group	Feature
I	1 Raising existing socket,

Raising Existing Socket

25 The items for raising existing socket shall in accordance with the Preamble to the Bill of Quantities General Directions include for:

Item coverage

(a) removing existing post;

(b) cleaning out socket;

(c) in situ concrete (as Section 17 paragraph 4);

(d) formwork (as Section 17 paragraph 14);

(e) loading, transporting from store, unloading, positioning and securing socket extension piece;

(f) refixing post.

Section 5: Drainage and Service Ducts

Definitions

1   The Earthworks Outline is defined in Section 6 Earthworks paragraphs 1 to 6 inclusive and shall apply equally to this Section.

2   Where the Existing Ground Level has been subjected to treatment, under the Contract, in respect of Ground Improvement, Mine Workings, Swallows Holes and the like, for the purpose of this Section Existing Ground Level shall be the level obtained upon completion of any such treatment of the areas affected.

3   Sub Soil Level is defined as the level of the ground after the removal of topsoil required by the Contract.

4   Surcharge is defined as material placed on embankments for the purpose of loading the embankment for the periods stated in the Contract.

Drains, Sewers, Piped Culverts and Service Ducts (excluding Filter and Fin Drains)

Units

5   The units of measurement for drains, sewers, piped culverts and service ducts shall be:

(i)   drains, sewers, piped culverts, service ducts .... linear metre.

Measurement

6   The measurement of drains, sewers, piped culverts and service ducts shall be the summation of their individual lengths measured along the centre lines of the pipes between any of the following:

(a)   the internal faces of chambers;

(b)   the external faces of headwalls;

(c)   the intersections of the centre lines at pipe junctions;

(d)   the centre of gully gratings (or where no grating is provided, the centre of the gulley);

(e)   the position of terminations shown in the Contract;

(f)   the point of change of stage depth.

7   The depth of drains, sewers, piped culverts and service ducts shall be the vertical measurement between the invert and the following:

(a)   where the invert level is below the Existing Ground Level—the Existing Ground Level except that where the Earthworks Outline is below the Existing Ground Level the measurement shall be taken to the Earthworks Outline;

(b)   where the invert is at or above the Existing Ground Level—to the datum stated in the Contract, or where none is stated, the Earthworks Outline;

8   The average depth to invert shall be the calculated arithmetic mean of the depths taken at intervals of 10 metres long the pipelines starting from the outfall end. For terminal lengths or pipelines less than 10 metres along the measurement of depths shall be taken at their ends.

9   The measurement of service ducts shall be for the complete construction irrespective of the number of ducts contained within any one trench.
Where more than one duct is laid in a trench then the number of ducts shall be stated in the item description.

Itemisation

10 Separate items shall be provided for drains, sewers, piped culverts and service ducts (excluding filter drains and fin drains) in accordance with Part II paragraphs 3 and 4 and the following:

Group		Feature
I	1	Drains or sewers.
	2	Piped culverts.
	3	Service ducts.
II	1	Different internal diameters.
III	1	Depths to invert not exceeding 2 metres. The average depth to invert to be stated to the nearest 25 mm.
	2	Depths to invert exceeding 2 metres but not exceeding 4 metres and so on in steps of 2 metres. The average depth to invert to be stated to the nearest 25 mm.
IV	1	Specified design groups.
	2	Particular designs stated in the Contract.
V	1	Construction in trench.
	2	Construction in heading.
	3	Construction by jacking or thrust boring.
	4	Suspended on discrete supports.
VI	1	In side slopes of cuttings or embankments.

Note: For each item which includes feature III 1 or III 2, an associated item shall be provided for adjustment of the rate for each 25 mm of difference in excess of 150 mm where the average depth to invert calculated from site measurement varies from that stated in the Bill of Quantities. The foregoing shall apply to both increases and decreases of average in excess of 150 mm.

Drains, Sewers, Piped Culverts and Service Ducts

Item coverage

11 The items for drains, sewers, piped culverts and service ducts shall in accordance with the Preambles to Bill of Quantities General Directions include for:

(a) excavation of acceptable material (as Section 6 paragraphs 16 and 17);

(b) excavation of unacceptable material (as Section 6 paragraph 18);

(c) access shafts to headings and their subsequent reinstatement;

(d) thrust pits and thrust blocks for pipe jacking and their removal on completion;

(e) pipes and fittings including cutting, laying, jointing and bedding;

(f) building in pipes to headwalls and outfall works;

(g) hangers, stools and discrete supports;

(h) bedding, haunching and surround;

(i) formwork (as Section 17 paragraph 14);

(j) backfilling and compaction;

(k) disposal of material (as Section 6 paragraph 32);

(l) movement joints to beds, surrounds and the like;

(m) reinstatement of unpaved areas;

(n) checking and cleaning;

(o) recording, staking and labelling;

(p) in the case of ducts fixing draw ropes, removable stoppers, marker blocks and posts;

(q) test certificates and supplying one copy to the Engineer.

Filter Drains

Units

12 The units of measurement for filter drains shall be:

(i) filter drains ....linear metre.

(ii) filter material contiguous with filter drains .... cubic metre.

Measurement

13 The measurement of filter drains shall be as for drains, sewers, piped culverts and service ducts.

14 The measurement of contiguous filter material shall be the volume of the material occupying the void between the filter drain and the adjacent carriageway hardshoulder and hardstrip. The side of the contiguous filter material next to the filter drain shall be taken as the vertical extension of the trench side above capping or where no capping is provided above sub grade level.

Itemisation

15 Separate items shall be provided for filter drains in accordance with Part II paragraphs 3 and 4 and the following:

Group	Feature	
I	1	Filter drains.
	2	Filter material contiguous with filter drains.
II	1	Different internal diameters.
	2	Different types of filter material.
III	1	Depths to invert not exceeding 2 metres. The average depth to invert to be stated to the nearest 25 mm.
	2	Depths to invert exceeding 2 metres but not exceeding 4 metres and so on in steps of 2 metres. The average depth to invert to be stated to the nearest 25 mm.
IV	1	Specified design groups.
	2	Particular designs stated in the Contract.
V	1	In side slopes of cuttings or embankments.

Note: For each item which includes feature III 1 or III 2 an associated item shall be provided for adjustment of the rate for each 25 mm of difference in excess of 150 mm where the average depth to invert calculated from site measurement varies from that stated in the Bill of Quantities. The foregoing shall apply to both increases and decreases of average in excess of 150 mm.

Filter Drains

16 The items for filter drains shall in accordance with the Preambles to Bill of Quantities General Directions include for:

Item coverage

(a) excavation of acceptable material (as Section 6 paragraphs 16 and 17);

(b) excavation of unacceptable material (as Section 6 paragraph 18);

(c) disposal of material (as Section 6 paragraph 32);

(d) pipes and fittings including cutting, laying, jointing and bedding;

(e) bedding, haunching and surround;

(f) formwork (as Section 17 paragraph 14);

(g) filter material and compaction;

(h) reinstatement of unpaved areas;

(i) checking and cleaning;

(j) recording, staking and labelling;

(k) permeable membrane;

(l) topsoiling, seeding and turfing.

Filter Material Contiguous with Filter Drains

17 The items for filter material contiguous with filter drains shall in accordance with the Preambles to Bill of Quantities General Directions include for:

Item coverage

(a) compaction;

(b) formwork (as Section 17 paragraph 14).

Fin Drains

Definition

18 The term fin drain shall be used for fin drains and shall include the alternative pipe and filter material whichever is used in the Works.

Units

19 The units of measurement shall be:

(i) fin drains .... linear metre.

Measurement

20 The measurement of fin drains shall be the length measured along the centre lines of the fin drains between any of the following:

(a) the internal faces of chambers;

(b) the position of terminations shown in the Contract.

The depth of the fin drain shall be the vertical measurement between the invert, and the Earthworks Outline.

Itemisation

21 Separate items shall be provided for fin drains in accordance with Part II paragraphs 3 and 4 and the following:

Group	Feature	
I	1	Fin drains.
II	1	Specified design group.
	2	Particular designs stated in the Contract.
III	1	Depth not exceeding 1.5 metres.

Fin Drains

22 The items for fin drains shall in accordance with the Preambles to Bill of Quantities General Directions include for:

Item coverage

(a) vertical membrane;

(b) filter drains (as this Section paragraph 16);

Connections

Units

23 The units of measurement for connections shall be:

(i) connections to existing drains, sewers, piped culverts, chambers, permanently severed land and mole drains .... number;

Measurement

24 The measurement of connections shall only be separately measured for connections to existing drains, sewers, piped culverts or chambers, and permanently severed land and mole drains.

Itemisation

25 Separate items shall be provided for connections in accordance with Part II paragraphs 3 and 4 and the following:

Group	Feature	
I	1	Connections to existing drains, sewers and piped culverts.
	2	Connections to existing chambers.
	3	Connections to permanently severed land and mole drains.
II	1	Different diameters.
III	1	Depths to invert not exceeding 2 metres.
	2	Depths to invert exceeding 2 metres but not exceeding 4 metres and so on in steps of 2 metres.

Connections to Existing Drains, Sewers, Piped Culverts, Chambers, Permanently Severed Land and Mole Drains

26 The items for connections to existing drains, sewers, piped culverts, chambers, permanently severed land and mole drains shall in accordance with the Preambles to Bill of Quantities General Directions include for:

Item coverage

(a) excavation of acceptable material (as Section 6 paragraphs 16 and 17);

(b) excavation of unacceptable material (as Section 6 paragraph 18);

(c) locating and making entry;

(d) backfilling and compaction;

(e) disposal of material (as Section 6 paragraph 32);

(f) making entry into chambers, concrete benching and channels, and making good the benching, channels and walls;

(g) locating severed ends of land and mole drains;

(h) pipes, fittings and saddles;

(i) bedding, haunching and surround, and filter material;

(j) formwork (as Section 17 paragraph 14);

(k) sealing off disused ends.

Chambers and Gullies.

Units

27 The units of measurement shall be:

(i) chambers, gullies .... number.

Measurement

28 The measurement shall be of the complete chamber or gully.

29 Depths of chambers shall be the distance between the top surface of the cover and the invert of the main channel, or where no channel is required by the Contract the uppermost surface of the base slab. Where no base slab is required the depth shall be taken to the bottom of the excavation.

Itemisation

30 Separate items shall be provided for chambers and gullies in accordance with Part II paragraphs 3 and 4 and the following:

Group	Feature	
I	1	Chambers.
	2	Gullies.
II	1	Specified design groups.
	2	Particular designs stated in the Contract.
III	1	Depths to invert not exceeding 1 metre.
	2	Depths to invert exceeding 1 metre but not exceeding 2 metres and so on in steps of 1 metre.
IV	1	Different types of covers or gratings.

Chambers

Item coverage

31 The items for chambers shall in accordance with the Preambles to Bill of Quantities General Directions include for:

(a) excavation of acceptable material (as Section 6 paragraphs 16 and 17);

(b) excavation of unacceptable material (as Section 6 paragraph 18);

(c) locating existing sewers and drains;

(d) construction of bases, walls, roof and cover slabs and shafts, surrounds and corbelling for cover;

(e) channels, fittings, benchings, building in pipes and fin drain connections;

(f) cleaning;

(g) step irons, safety chains, ladders, handholds and the like;

(h) covers, frames, seatings and bedding;

(i) cover keys;

(j) concrete (as Section 17 paragraphs 4 and 9);

(k) formwork (as Section 17 paragraph 14);

(l) reinforcement (as Section 17 paragraph 25);

(m) backfilling and compaction;

(n) disposal of material (as Section 6 paragraph 32);

(o) soakaway filling material.

Gullies

Item coverage

32 The items for gullies shall in accordance with the Preambles to Bill of Quantities General Directions include for:

(a) excavation of acceptable material (as section 6 paragraphs 16 and 17);

(b) excavation of unacceptable material (as Section 6 paragraph 18);

(c) fittings including in situ concrete (as Section 17 paragraph 4) bed and surround and jointing to pipes;

(d) gratings, frames, seatings and bedding;

(e) formwork (as Section 17 paragraph 14);

(f) cleaning;

(g) backfilling and compaction;

(h) disposal of material (as Section 6 paragraph 32).

Surface Water Channels

Units

33 The units of measurement shall be:

(i) surface water channels .... linear metre.

Measurement **34** The measurement of surface water channels shall be the length along the centre line of the channel. No deduction shall be made for gaps of 1 linear metre or less.

Itemisation **35** Separate items shall be provided for surface water channels in accordance with Part II paragraphs 3 and 4 and the following:

Group	Feature	
I	1	Surface water channels.
II	1	Specified design type.
	2	Particular designs stated in the Contract.

Surface Water Channels **36** The items for surface water channels shall in accordance with the Preambles to Bill of Quantities General Directions include for:

Item coverage

(a) excavation of acceptable material (as Section 6 paragraphs 16 and 17);

(b) excavation of unacceptable material (as Section 6 paragraph 18);

(c) concrete (as Section 17 paragraphs 4 and 9);

(d) formwork (as Section 17 paragraph 14);

(e) reinforcement (as Section 17 paragraph 25);

(f) gratings, frames, seatings and bedding;

(g) tie bars;

(h) drainage layer;

(i) drainage holes or pipes through concrete;

(j) disposal of material (as Section 6 paragraph 32);

(k) additional pavement material below channels;

(l) backfilling and compaction.

Combined Drainage and Kerb Blocks

Units **37** The units of measurement shall be:

(i) combined drainage and kerb blocks .... linear metre.

Measurement **38** The measurement of combined drainage and kerb blocks shall be the length along the centre line of the combined drainage and kerb blocks. No deduction shall be made for gaps of 1 linear metre or less.

Itemisation **39** Separate items shall be provided for combined drainage and kerb blocks in accordance with Part II paragraphs 3 and 4 and the following:

Group	Feature	
I	1	Combined drainage and kerb blocks.
II	1	Specified design type.
	2	Particular designs stated in the Contract.

Combined Drainage and Kerb Blocks **40** The items for combined drainage and kerb blocks shall in accordance with the Preambles to Bill of Quantities General Directions include for:

Item coverage
- (a) surface water channels (as this Section paragraph 36);
- (b) special units and fittings;
- (c) connections to chambers;
- (d) cleaning.

Drainage Channel Blocks

Units

41 The units of measurement shall be:

(i) Drainage channel blocks .... linear metre.

Measurement

42 The measurement of drainage channel blocks shall be the length along the centre line of the drainage channel blocks.
No deductions shall be made for gaps of 1 linear metre or less.

Itemisation

43 Separate items shall be provided for drainage channel blocks in accordance with Part II paragraphs 3 and 4 and the following:

Group		Feature
I	1	Drainage channel blocks.
II	1	Specified design type.
	2	Particular designs stated in the Contract.

Drainage Channel Blocks

44 The items for drainage channel blocks shall in accordance with the Preambles to Bill of Quantities General Directions include for:

Item coverage

(a) combined drainage and kerb blocks (as this Section paragraph 40).

Headwalls and Outfall Works

Units
Measurement
Itemisation

45 Except for small headwalls and the like to smaller pipes, headwalls and outfall works and the like shall be measured in accordance with the units of measurement, measurement and itemisation set out in the relevant Sections of the Method of Measurement.

Small Headwalls

Units

46 The units of measurement shall be:

(i) small headwall and the like .... number.

Itemisation

47 Separate items shall be provided for small headwall and the like in accordance with Part II paragraphs 3 and 4 and the following:

Group		Feature
I	1	Small headwall.
	2	Small revetment.
II	1	Different types.
III	1	Pipe not exceeding 100 mm internal diameter.
	2	Pipe exceeding 100 mm but not exceeding 300 mm internal diameter.

Small Headwall and the like

Item coverage

48 The items for small headwall and the like shall in accordance with the Preambles to Bill of Quantities General Directions include for:

(a) brickwork, copings, string courses and the like (as Section 24 paragraph 4);

(b) blockwork, stonework, copings, string courses individual blocks, features or stones (as Section 24 paragraph 8);

(c) lining of watercourses (as Section 6 paragraph 83);

(d) drainage channel blocks (as this Section paragraph 44).

Soft Spots and Other Voids

Units

49 The units of measurement shall be:

(i) soft spots, other voids .... cubic metre.

Measurement

50 The measurement of soft spots and other voids shall be the volume of the void directed to be excavated or filled. For this measurement the width shall be taken for drains, sewers, piped culverts, service ducts and filter drains, as the internal diameter of the pipe plus 600 mm. Where no pipe is required the width shall be taken as 600 mm. For chambers, gullies and the like the measurement shall be taken as the horizontal area of the base slab or where no base slab is required the bottom of the excavation. The depths shall be measured from the underside of the thinnest permitted bed in any one group for trenches and from the underside of the base slab for chambers, gullies and the like.

Itemisation

51 Separate items shall be provided for soft spots and other voids in accordance with Part II paragraphs 3 and 4 and the following:

Group	Feature	
I	1	Excavation of soft spots and other voids.
	2	Filling of soft spots and other voids.
II	1	Different types of fill.

Excavation of Soft Spots and Other Voids

Item coverage

52 The items for excavation of soft spots and other voids shall in accordance with the Preambles to Bill of Quantities General Directions include for:

(a) excavation of acceptable material (as Section 6 paragraphs 16 and 17);

(b) excavation of unacceptable material (as Section 6 paragraph 18);

(c) disposal of material (as Section 6 paragraph 32);

Filling of Soft Spots and Other Voids

Item coverage

53 The items for filling of soft spots and other voids shall in accordance with the Preambles to Bill of Quantities General Directions include for:

(a) deposition of fill (as Section 6 paragraph 27);

(b) compaction of fill (as Section 6 paragraph 45);

(c) in situ concrete (as Section 17 paragraph 4);

(d) formwork (as Section 17 paragraph 14).

Supports left in Excavation

Units

54 The units of measurement shall be:

(i) supports left in excavation .... square metre.

Measurement | **55** Measurement shall be the area of face required by the Contract to be left with supports in position.

Itemisation | **56** Separate items shall be provided for supports left in excavation in accordance with Part II paragraphs 3 and 4 and the following:

Group		Feature
I	1	Supports.
II	1	Timber.
	2	Steel.
III	1	Different types.
IV	1	Construction in trench.
	2	Construction in pits.
	3	Construction in heading.

Supports left in Excavation

57 The items for supports left in excavation shall in accordance with the Preambles to Bill of Quantities General Directions include for:

Item coverage | (a) struts, walings and the like and working around them.

Drainage and Service Ducts in Structures (including Reinforced Earth Structures and Anchored Earth Structures)

Units | **58** The units of measurement shall be:

(i) drainage and service ducts in structures .... item.

Measurement | **59** The components comprising the items of drainage and service ducts in structures shall be identified and scheduled in the Contract.

Itemisation | **60** Separate items shall be provided for drainage and service ducts in structures in accordance with Part II paragraphs 3 and 4 and the following:

Group		Feature
I	1	Drainage.
	2	Service ducts.
II	1	Substructure—End supports.
	2	Substructure—Intermediate supports.
	3	Superstructure.
	4	Reinforced earth structure.
	5	Anchored earth structure.

Drainage and Service Ducts in Structures

Item coverage

61 The items for drainage and service ducts in structures shall in accordance with the Preambles to Bill of Quantities General Directions include for:

(a) drains, sewers, piped culverts and service ducts (as this Section paragraph 11);

(b) chambers (as this Section paragraph 31);

(c) gullies (as this Section paragraph 32);

(d) pipework, gullies, downpipes, fittings and the like including brackets, hangers and straps, fixing to or building into the structure;

(e) making good protective system, waterproofing;

(f) permeable backing including compaction and supports;

(g) channels.

Filling to Pipe Bays and Verges on Bridges

Units

62 The units of measurement shall be:

(i) filling to pipe bays and verges on bridges ....cubic metre.

Measurement

63 The measurement shall be the volume of the void stated in the Contract to be filled except that no deduction shall be made for drains, sewers, service ducts, services, supplies and the like and their supports.

Itemisation

64 Separate items shall be provided for filling to pipe bays and verges on bridges in accordance with Part II paragraphs 3 and 4 and the following:

Group	Feature	
I	1	Filling to pipe bays and verges on bridges.
II	1	Different types.

Filling to Pipe Bays and Verges on Bridges

Item coverage

65 The items for filling to pipe bays and verges on bridges shall in accordance with the Preambles to Bill of Quantities General Directions include for:

(a) deposition;

(b) complying with any restrictions on the placing and compacting of materials;

(c) compaction around drains, sewers, service ducts, services, supplies, supports and the like.

Raising or Lowering Covers and Gratings on Existing Chambers and Gullies

Units

66 The units of measurement shall be:

(i) raising or lowering covers and gratings on existing chambers and gullies .... number.

Itemisation

67 Separate items shall be provided for raising or lowering covers and gratings on existing chambers and gullies in accordance with Part II paragraphs 3 and 4 and the following:

Group		Feature
I	1	Raising the level.
	2	Lowering the level.
II	1	Different sizes of cover.
	2	Different sizes of grating.
III	1	Different types of cover.
	2	Different types of grating.
IV	1	Different sizes of chamber.
	2	Different sizes of gully.
V	1	Different construction of chamber.
	2	Different construction of gully.
VI	1	Not exceeding 150 mm.
	2	Exceeding 150 mm but not exceeding 300 mm and so on in steps of 150 mm.

Raising or Lowering Covers and Gratings on Existing Chambers and Gullies

68 The items for raising or lowering covers and gratings on existing chambers or gullies shall in accordance with the Preambles to Bill of Quantities General Directions include for:

Item coverage

(a) excavation of acceptable material (as Section 6 paragraphs 16 and 17);

(b) excavation of unacceptable material (as Section 6 paragraph 18);

(c) take up existing cover or grating including frame and clean and set aside for re-use;

(d) demolition and preparation to receive new construction;

(e) construction of walls, roof and cover slabs and shafts surrounds and corbelling for cover and making good;

(f) step irons, safety chains, ladders, handholds and the like;

(g) bedding existing cover or grating including frame;

(h) concrete (as Section 17 paragraphs 4 and 9);

(i) formwork (as Section 17 paragraph 14);

(j) reinforcement (as Section 17 paragraph 25);

(k) backfilling and compaction;

(l) disposal of material (as Section 6 paragraph 32);

(m) taking precautions to avoid damage to drains and sewers;

(n) cleaning;

(o) reinstatement of adjacent surfaces;

Remove from Store and Reinstall Chamber Covers and Frames, and Gully Gratings and Frames

Units

69 The units of measurement shall be:

(i) remove from store and reinstall chamber covers and frames, gully gratings and frames .... number.

Measurement

70 The measurement of remove from store and reinstall chamber covers and frames and gully gratings and frames shall be the complete installation.

Itemisation

71 Separate items shall be provided for remove from store and reinstall chamber covers and frames and gully gratings and frames in accordance with Part II paragraphs 3 and 4 include for:

Group	Feature	
I	1	Different types of chamber covers and frames.
	2	Different types of gully gratings and frames.
II	1	Different sizes.

Remove from Store and Reinstall Chamber Covers and Frames and Gully Gratings and Frames

72 The items for remove from store and reinstall chamber covers and frames and gully gratings and frames shall in accordance with the Preambles to Bill of Quantities General Directions include for:

Item coverage

(a) loading, transporting from store, unloading and positioning for reinstallation;

(b) replacing items damaged during the foregoing operations;

(c) modification and new materials;

(d) raising or lowering covers and gratings on existing chambers and gullies (as this Section paragraph 68).

Grouting up of Existing Drains, Sewers, Piped Culverts and Service Ducts

Units

73 The units of measurement shall be:

(i) grouting up of existing drains, sewers, piped culverts and service ducts .... linear metre.

Measurement

74 The measurement of grouting up of existing drains, sewers, piped culverts and service ducts shall be the length to be grouted as stated in the Contract.

Itemisation

75 Separate items shall be provided for grouting up of existing drains, sewers, piped culverts and service ducts in accordance with Part II paragraphs 3 and 4 and the following:

Group	Feature	
I	1	Grouting up of existing drains, sewers, piped culverts and service ducts.
II	1	Different diameters.
III	1	Different types of grout.

Grouting Up of Existing Drains, Sewers, Piped Culverts and Service Ducts

76 The items for grouting up of existing drains, sewers, piped culverts and service ducts shall in accordance with the Preambles to Bill of Quantities General Directions include for:

Item coverage

(a) excavation in acceptable material (as Section 6 paragraphs 16 and 17);

(b) excavation in unacceptable material (as Section 6 paragraph 18);

(c) breaking into drain, sewer, piped culvert or service duct and cleaning;

(d) mixing and placing grout;

(e) in situ concrete (as Section 17 paragraph 4);

(f) formwork (as Section 17 paragraph 14);

(g) backfilling and compaction;

(h) disposal of material (as Section 6 paragraph 32).

Excavation in Hard Material

Units

77 The units of measurement shall be:

(i) excavation in hard material .... cubic metre. Measured extra over main construction.

Measurement

78 The measurement shall be the volume of the voids formed by the removal of the hard material. For this measurement the width shall be taken for drains, sewers, piped culverts, service ducts and filter drains as the internal diameter of the pipe plus 600 mm. Where no pipe is required the width shall be taken as 600 mm. For chambers, gullies and the like the measurement shall be taken as the horizontal area of the base slab or where no base slab is required the area of the bottom of the excavation.

Itemisation

79 Separate items shall be provided for excavation in hard material in accordance with Part II paragraphs 3 and 4 and the following:

Group	Feature
I	1 Excavation in hard material.

Excavation in Hard Material

80 The items for excavation in hard material shall in accordance with the Preambles to Bill of Quantities General Directions include for:

Item coverage

(a) Excavation of hard material (as Section 6 paragraph 22).

Section 6: Earthworks

Definitions

1   The Earthworks Outline, unless expressly stated otherwise, is defined as the finished earthworks levels and dimensions (prior to topsoiling) required by the Contract for the construction, where specified, of:

(a) carriageway, hard shoulder, hardstrip, footway, paved area, central reserve, verge, side slope;

(b) sub base material, fill on sub base material, roadbase and capping;

(c) contiguous filter material;

(d) surface water channels;

(e) landscape areas, noise bunds.

In all cases of filter drains the Earthworks Outline shall be the top of the filter material.

2   Where capping or stabilisation to form capping is required by the Contract to be constructed in cutting or on embankment—the Earthworks Outline shall be as defined in paragraph 1 of this Section as the top of capping.

3   Where an embankment is required by the Contract to be surcharged—the Earthworks Outline shall be as defined in paragraph 1 of this Section and exclude the surcharge.

4   Where permanent storage or stockpiling of topsoil is required by the Contract—the Earthworks Outline shall be as defined in paragraph 1 of this Section and exclude stored topsoil.

5   Where the bottom of a structural foundation for an earth retaining structure (other than for reinforced earth and an anchored earth structure) is below Existing Ground Level—the Earthworks Outline shall be the permanently exposed face of the structure below Existing Ground Level.

6   Where the bottom of the facing foundation for a reinforced earth structure or an anchored earth structure is below Existing Ground Level—the Earthworks Outline shall be the inside face of the facing above Existing Ground Level to the underside of the capping unit, or where no capping unit is required, to the finished earthworks level prior to topsoiling.

7   Where the Existing Ground Level has been subjected to treatment under the Contract in respect of Ground Improvement, Mine Workings, Swallow Holes and the like, for the purpose of this Section Existing Ground Level shall be the level obtained upon completion of any such treatment of the areas affected.

8   Sub-Soil Level is defined as the level of the ground after the removal of topsoil required by the Contract.

9   Surcharge is defined as material placed on embankments for the purpose of loading the embankment for the periods stated in the Contract.

Measurement General

10   For the purpose of this Section it shall be assumed that one cubic metre of material excavated forms one cubic metre of compacted fill. No allowance shall be made in the measurement for bulking and shrinkage of any material.

11   For the purpose of this Section no account shall be taken of excavated material arising from the Works measured in accordance with Sections 1 to 5 and 7 to 26 hereof.

12   Where deposition and compaction of an embankment has been carried out in accordance with the Contract and settlement occurs:

(a) subsequent to Earthworks Outline having being reached, or in the case of a surcharged embankment subsequent to the removal of the surcharge; or

(b) from settlement of or penetration into the ground beneath the embankment,
then the additional fill, deposition and compaction required shall be measured immediately prior to the preparation of formation, provided that the first 75 mm of settlement or penetration shall not be measured.

In the case of landscape areas, noise bunds and other areas of fill where settlement or penetration occurs the additional fill deposition and compaction required shall not be measured.

Excavation

Units

13 The units of excavation shall be:

(i) excavation .... cubic metre.

Measurement

14 The measurement of excavation shall be, for:

(a) topsoil Class 5A—the volume of the void formed by the excavation of material to Sub-Soil Level;

(b) cutting and other excavation:

(i) cutting and bulk excavation—the volume of the void formed by the excavation of material from Existing Ground Level down to Earthworks Outline, together with the volume of the void formed by the excavation of material below that Outline; or

(ii) under embankments, and other areas of fill—the volume of the void formed by the excavation of material below Existing Ground Level;

less in each case the volume of topsoil Class 5A in the void included in the measurement under paragraph 14(a). The volume of excavation of soft spots measured under paragraph 55 of this Section shall not be included.

(c) removal of surcharge—the volume of material remaining as surcharge to be removed down to the datum stated in the Contract, or if none is stated, to the Earthworks Outline.

(d) structural foundations—the volume of the void to accommodate the structural foundation calculated on the basis of the horizontal area of the bottom of the foundation with the depth being measured from the bottom of the foundation (including blinding concrete) to:

(i) where the bottom of the foundation is below Existing Ground Level—the Existing Ground Level. Provided that where the Earthworks Outline is below Existing Ground Level the depth shall be measured to the Earthworks Outline;

(ii) where the bottom of the foundation is at or above Existing Ground Level—the datum stated in the Contract, or where none is stated to Earthworks Outline,

less in each case the volume of topsoil Class 5A in the void included in the measurement under paragraph 14(a). The volume of excavation of soft spots measured under paragraph 55 of this Section shall not be included.

The classification of stage depths for the excavation of structural foundations shall be the maximum depth of excavation obtained in accordance with this sub paragraph.

(e) foundations for corrugated steel structures and the like—the volume of the void to accommodate the structure, bedding and surround down to the outline stated in the Contract from:

(i) where the bottom of the bedding is below Existing Ground Level—from Existing Ground Level.

(ii) where the bottom of the bedding is at or above Existing Ground Level—from the datum stated in the Contract or where none is stated to Earthworks Outline,

less in each case the volume of topsoil Class 5A in the void included in the measurement under paragraph 14(a). The volume of the excavation of soft spots measured under paragraph 55 of this Section shall not be included.

The classification of stage depths for the excavation of the foundation shall be the maximum depth of excavation obtained in accordance with this sub paragraph.

(f) new and enlarged watercourses, intercepting ditches,—the volume of the void formed from Existing Ground Level down to the outline stated in the Contract less the volume of topsoil Class 5A in the void included in the measurement under paragraph 14a of this Section.

(g) clearing abandoned watercourses—the volume of the void formed from Existing Ground Level down to the outline stated in the Contract.

Itemisation

15 Separate items shall be provided for excavation in accordance with Part II paragraphs 3 and 4, and the following:

Group	Feature	
I	1	Excavation.
II	1	Acceptable material Class 5A.
	2	Acceptable material Class 3.
	3	Acceptable material excluding Classes 3 and 5A.
	4	Unacceptable material Class U1.
	5	Unacceptable material Class U2.
III	1	Cutting and other excavation.
	2	Structural foundations.
	3	Foundations for corrugated steel structures and the like.
	4	New watercourses.
	5	Enlarged watercourses.
	6	Intercepting ditches.
	7	Clearing abandoned watercourses.
	8	Removal of surcharge.
IV	1	0 metres to 3 metres in depth.
	2	0 metres to 6 metres in depth and so on in steps of 3 metres.

Note 1: Acceptable material Class 5A shall not be separately identified by any Group III or IV Feature.
Note 2: Group IV Features shall be applied only to Features 2 and 3 of Group III.

Excavation of Acceptable Material Class 5A

16 The items for excavation of acceptable material Class 5A shall in accordance with the Preambles to Bill of Quantities General Directions include for:

Item coverage

(a) loading into transport;

(b) multiple handling of material;

(c) keeping earthworks free of water;

(d) haulage and deposition in temporary stockpiles including the provision of sites for stockpiles;

(e) taking precautions to avoid damage to property, structures, drains, sewers, services, instrumentation and the like;

(f) grading beds and trimming side slopes of watercourses and the like.

Excavation of Acceptable Material Class 3, Acceptable Material Excluding Classes 3 and 5A

17 The items for excavation of acceptable material Class 3 and acceptable material excluding Classes 3 and 5A shall in accordance with the Preambles to Bill of Quantities General Directions include for:

Item coverage

(a) loosening or breaking up material before or in the process of excavation;

(b) upholding the sides;

(c) working around and between piles;

(d) overbreak and making good;

(e) keeping earthworks free of water;

(f) selection and separation of materials;

(g) forming and trimming side slopes, benchings and berms;

(h) trimming the bottom and sides of foundations;

(i) grading beds and trimming sides of watercourses and the like;

(j) protection of sub-grade;

(k) additional excavation the Contractor may require for working space, timbering, formwork or other temporary works and its subsequent backfilling with approved materials and compaction;

(l) taking precautions to avoid damage to property, structures, drains, sewers, services, instrumentation and the like;

(m) treatment of faces of cuttings which are not to receive topsoil;

(n) loading into transport;

(o) multiple handling of material;

(p) disposal of surcharge material (as this Section paragraph 32);

(q) waiting for frozen material to thaw;

(r) replacing acceptable material rendered unacceptable;

(s) breaking down material necessary to comply with the requirements of fill;

(t) haulage deposition and compaction in temporary stockpiles including provision of sites for stockpiles;

(u) complying with special requirements for Class 3 material.

Excavation of Unacceptable Material Classes U1 and U2

18 The items for excavation of unacceptable material Class U1 and unacceptable material Class U2 shall in accordance with the Preamble to Bill of Quantities General Directions include for:

Item coverage

(a) excavation (as this Section paragraph 17(a) to (p) inclusive).

(b) special measures for dealing with Class U2 material.

Excavation in Hard Material

Units

19 The units of measurement shall be:

(i) extra over excavation for excavation in hard material .... cubic metre.

Measurement

20 The measurement for extra over excavation for excavation in hard material shall be the volume of the voids formed by the removal of the hard material.

Itemisation

21 Separate items shall be provided for extra over excavation for excavation in hard material in accordance with Part II paragraphs 3 and 4 and the following:

Group		Feature
I	1	Extra over excavation for excavation in hard material.
II	1	Cutting and other excavation.
	2	Structural foundations.
	3	Foundations for corrugated steel structures and the like.
	4	New watercourses.
	5	Enlarged watercourses.
	6	Intercepting ditches.
	7	Clearing abandoned watercourses.

Extra Over Excavation for Excavation in Hard Material

22 The items for extra over excavation for excavation in hard material shall in accordance with the Preambles to Bill of Quantities General Directions include for:

Item coverage

(a) preliminary site trials of blasting;

(b) blasting, splitting, breaking and the like;

(c) cutting through reinforcement;

(d) saw cutting and trimming;

(e) treatment to bottoms of foundations.

Deposition of Fill

Units

23 The units of measurement shall be:

(i) deposition of fill .... cubic metres.

Measurement

24 The measurement of deposition of fill shall be the volume of compacted fill, calculated in accordance with paragraphs 40, 41 and 42 of this Section, less the volume of imported fill calculated in accordance with paragraphs 34 and 35 of this Section.

25 Deposition of Class 1C and 6B materials shall be separately measured only where Class 1C or 6B material as such is specifically stated by the Contract to be required to be placed in a particular location.

Itemisation

26 Separate items shall be provided for deposition of fill in accordance with Part II paragraphs 3 and 4 and the following:

Group		Feature
I	1	Deposition.
II	1	Acceptable material.
	2	Acceptable material Class 1C.
	3	Acceptable material Class 3.
	4	Acceptable material Class 6B.
III	1	Embankments and other areas of fill.
	2	Strengthened embankments.
	3	Reinforced earth structures.
	4	Anchored earth structures.
	5	Landscape areas.
	6	Noise bunds.
	7	Fill to structures.
	8	Fill above structural concrete foundations.
	9	Fill on sub base material, roadbase and capping.
	10	Fill on bridges (under footways, verges and central reserves).
	11	Upper bedding to corrugated steel structures and the like.
	12	Lower bedding to corrugated steel structures and the like.
	13	Surround to corrugated steel structures and the like.

Deposition of Fill

27 The items for deposition of fill shall in accordance with the Preambles to Bill of Quantities General Directions include for:

Item coverage

(a) compaction of fill (as this Section paragraph 45(a) to (g) inclusive);

(b) haulage;

(c) waiting for frozen material to thaw;

(d) replacing acceptable material rendered unacceptable;

(e) selection of material of stated Classes and layering or depositing in locations stated in the Contract;

(f) depositing fill to slope away from vertical drainage layers and measures to prevent surface water entering such layers;

(g) mechanical or chemical treatment of soil as the Contractor may require to facilitate the use of particular plant;

(h) trimming and shaping to levels and contours;

(i) deposition of fill resulting from settlement and penetration of landscape areas, noise bunds and other areas of fill, and from the first 75 mm of settlement and penetration of embankments.

Disposal of Material

Units

28 The units of measurement shall be:

(i) disposal of material .... cubic metre.

Measurement

29 The measurement of disposal of acceptable material shall be the volume of acceptable material excluding topsoil Class 5A, excavated from within the Site measured in this Section less the volume of compacted fill calculated in accordance with paragraphs 40, 41 and 42 of this Section, after deduction from the latter of the volume of imported fill calculated in accordance with paragraphs 34 and 35 of this Section.

30 The measurement of disposal of unacceptable material shall be the volume of unacceptable material excavated from within the Site and measured in this Section.

Itemisation

31 Separate items shall be provided for disposal of material in accordance with Part II paragraphs 3 and 4 and the following:

Group	Feature	
I	1	Disposal.
II	1	Acceptable material excluding Class 5A.
	2	Unacceptable material Class U1.
	3	Unacceptable material Class U2.

Disposal of Material

32 The items for disposal of material shall in accordance with the Preambles to Bill of Quantities General Directions include for:

Item coverage

(a) haulage and deposition in tips off Site provided by the Contractor;

(b) multiple handling of material;

(c) special measures for dealing with Class U2 material;

(d) allowing for deposition in lieu of disposal of acceptable fill resulting from settlement and penetration of landscape areas, noise bunds and other areas of fill, and from the first 75 mm of settlement and penetration of embankments.

Imported Fill

Units

33 The units of measurement shall be:

(i) imported fill .... cubic metre.

Measurement

34 The measurement of imported acceptable fill shall be the volume of compacted fill, calculated in accordance with paragraphs 40, 41 and 42 of this Section less the volumes of:

(a) acceptable material, excluding topsoil Class 5A excavated from within the Site and measured in this Section;

(b) other stated classes of imported acceptable fill excluding topsoil Class 5B.

35 The measurement of other stated classes of imported acceptable fill, other than topsoil Class 5B, shall be the volume of the void filled with the stated class of imported acceptable fill to the outline stated in the Contract.

36 The measurement of imported topsoil Class 5B shall be the volume of topsoil calculated from the areas and thicknesses to be topsoiled less the volume of topsoil Class 5A excavated from within the Site and measured in accordance with paragraph 14(a) of this Section.

Itemisation

37 Separate items shall be provided for imported acceptable fill in accordance with Part II paragraphs 3 and 4 and the following:

Group		Feature
I	1	Imported acceptable material.
	2	Other stated classes of imported acceptable fill.
	3	Imported topsoil Class 5B.
II	1	Embankments and other areas of fill.
	2	Strengthened embankments.
	3	Reinforced earth structures.
	4	Anchored earth structures.
	5	Landscape areas.
	6	Noise bunds.
	7	Fill to structures.
	8	Fill above structural concrete foundations.
	9	Fill on sub base material, roadbase and capping.
	10	Fill on bridges (under footways, verges, and central reserves).
	11	Upper bedding to corrugated steel structures and the like.
	12	Lower bedding to corrugated steel structures and the like.
	13	Surround to corrugated steel structures and the like.

Note: Group I Feature 3 Imported topsoil Class 5B shall not be separately identified by any Group II Feature.

Imported Fill

38 The items for imported fill shall in accordance with the Preambles to Bill of Quantities General Directions include for:

Item coverage

(a) compaction of fill (as this Section paragraph 45(a) to (g) inclusive);

(b) fill provided by the Contractor from sources outside the Site;

(c) replacing acceptable material rendered unacceptable;

(d) selection of material of stated Classes and layering or depositing in locations stated in the Contract;

(e) depositing fill to slope away from vertical drainage layers and measures to prevent surface water entering such layers;

(f) trimming and shaping to levels and contours;

(g) imported fill resulting from settlement and penetration of landscape areas, noise bunds and other areas of fill, and from the first 75 mm of settlement and penetration of embankments.

Compaction of Fill

Units

39 The units of measurement shall be:

(i) compaction of fill .... cubic metres.

Measurement

40 The measurement of compaction of fill in embankments and other areas of fill, in strengthened embankments, in reinforced earth structures, in anchored earth structures, in landscape areas and in noise bunds shall be the volume of the embankment or void filled from Existing Ground Level up to the Earthworks Outline plus, where required by the Contract, the volume of:

(a) the void formed by the removal of topsoil Class 5A beneath the fill in question, and included in the measurement under paragraph 14(a) of this Section;

(b) the void formed by excavation for the fill in question;

    (i) below Earthworks Outline included in the measurement under paragraph 14(b)(i) of this Section; and

    (ii) below Existing Ground Level included in the measurement under paragraph 14(b)(ii) of this Section.

(c) surcharge, being the void filled from the Earthworks Outline up to the profile stated in the Contract to which the surcharge is required to be constructed,

less in each case the volume of any compaction of fill to structures, and bedding and surround to corrugated steel structures and the like included in the volume so obtained and which is measured separately under paragraph 42 of this Section.

41 The measurement of compaction of fill above structural concrete foundations shall be the volume of the void measured in accordance with paragraph 14(d) of this Section less the volume of the structural foundation and structure within that void.

42 The measurement of compaction of:

(a) fill to structures;

(b) fill on sub base material, roadbase and capping;

(c) fill on bridges (under footways, verges and central reserves);

(d) bedding to corrugated steel structures and the like;

(e) surround to corrugated steel structures and the like;

in each case, shall be the volume of the void filled to the outline stated in the Contract less the volume of corrugated steel structures and the like within that void.

43 Compaction of Class 1C and 6B materials shall be separately measured only where Class 1C or 6B material as such is specifically stated by the Contract to be required to be placed in a particular location.

Itemisation

44 Separate items shall be provided for compaction of fill in accordance with Part II paragraphs 3 and 4 and the following:

Group	Feature	
I	1	Compaction.
II	1	Acceptable material.
	2	Acceptable material Class 1C.
	3	Acceptable material Class 3.
	4	Acceptable material Class 6B.
III	1	Embankments and other areas of fill.
	2	Strengthened embankments.
	3	Reinforced earth structures.
	4	Anchored earth structures.
	5	Landscape areas.
	6	Noise bunds.
	7	Fill to structures.
	8	Fill above structural concrete foundations.
	9	Fill on sub base material, roadbase and capping.
	10	Fill on bridges (under footways, verges and central reserves).
	11	Upper bedding to corrugated steel structures and the like.
	12	Lower bedding to corrugated steel structures and the like.
	13	Surround to corrugated steel structures and the like.

Compaction of Fill

45 The items for compaction of fill shall in accordance with the Preambles to Bill of Quantities General Directions include for:

Item coverage

(a) protection of sub grade;

(b) multiple handling of material;

(c) keeping earthworks free of water;

(d) complying with requirements and constraints on the sequence, timing and rate of deposition and filling, and equalisation of earth pressures;

(e) complying with the special requirements for Class 3 material;

(f) complying with the particular requirements and constraints with regard to reinforced earth structures, strengthened embankments, anchored earth structures, soil stabilisation, corrugated steel structures and the like;

(g) taking precautions to avoid damage to property, structures, sewers, drains, services instrumentation and the like;

(h) spreading and levelling;

(i) compaction trials and demonstrations;

(j) forming and trimming side slopes, benchings and berms;

(k) blinding and treatment of side slopes and berms;

(l) compaction of fill resulting from settlement and penetration of landscape areas, noise bunds and other areas of fill, and from the first 75 mm of settlement and penetration of embankments.

Soil Stabilisation

Units

46 The units of measurement shall be:

(i) soil stabilisation .... cubic metre.

Measurement

47 The measurement of soil stabilisation shall be the volume of the material to be stabilised measured to the outlines stated in the Contract irrespective of the number of layers or thicknesses, methods or sequences of operations involved in stabilising the material to the depth required.

Note: Soil stabilisation means the process of stabilisation whether the material is intact and undisturbed or deposited and compacted prior to stabilisation.

Excavation, fill, import, disposal, deposition and compaction required to expose or produce the layer to be stabilised, as appropriate, shall be included in the measurement of Earthworks elsewhere in this Section.

Excavation, deposition and compaction involved in the process of stabilisation itself shall not be measured.

Itemisation

48 Separate items shall be provided for soil stabilisation in accordance with Part II paragraphs 3 and 4 and the following:

Group	Feature
I	1 Soil stabilisation.
II	1 Capping.
III	1 Cement. 2 Lime.

Soil Stabilisation with Cement, Soil Stabilisation with Lime

49 The items for soil stabilisation shall in accordance with the Preambles to Bill of Quantities General Directions include for:

Item coverage

(a) excavation of acceptable material (as this Section Paragraphs 16 and 17);

(b) deposition (as this Section Paragraph 27);

(c) compaction of fill (as this Section Paragraph 45);

(d) pulverising, measuring and mixing;

(e) laps and joints;

(f) curing, protection and sealing;

(g) shaping to cambers, falls and crowns;

(h) edge supports;

(i) additional fill, deposition, compaction or disposal resulting from the process of stabilisation;

(j) additional fill and stabilisation resulting from the first 75 mm of settlement and penetration of embankments.

Geotextiles

Units

50 The units of measurement shall be:

(i) geotextile ....square metre.

Measurement

51 The measurement of geotextile shall be the area covered by the geotextile.

Itemisation

52 Separate item shall be provided for geotextile in accordance with Part II paragraphs 3 and 4 and the following:

Group	Feature
I	1 Geotextile.
II	1 Different types.
III	1 Different grades.

Geotextile

53 The items for geotextile shall in accordance with Preambles to Bill of Quantities General Directions include for:

Item coverage

(a) cleaning, trimming, regulating and preparing surfaces;

(b) laps;

(c) measures to protect material;

(d) jointing, sealing and fixing;

(e) securing material in place;

(f) complying with the requirements of strengthened earthworks;

(g) turn ups and overlaps at edges.

Soft Spots and Other Voids

Units

54 The units of measurement shall be:

(i) soft spots, other voids..........cubic metre.

Measurement

55 The measurement of soft spots and other voids shall be the volume of the void directed to be excavated or filled. Soft spots and other voids shall be measured separately from the main excavation or filling where the volume:

(a) below structural foundations or in side slopes of cuttings is less than 1 cubic metre; and

(b) elsewhere is less than 25 cubic metres.

Itemisation

56 Separate items shall be provided for soft spots and other voids in accordance with Part II paragraphs 3 and 4 and the following:

Group	Feature	
I	1	Excavation of soft spots and other voids.
	2	Filling of soft spots and other voids.
II	1	Below cuttings or under embankments.
	2	In side slopes.
	3	Below structural foundations.
III	1	Different types of fill.

Excavation of Soft Spots

Item coverage

57 The items for excavation of soft spots and other voids shall in accordance with the Preambles to Bill of Quantities General Directions include for:

(a) excavation of acceptable material (as this Section paragraphs 16 and 17);

(b) excavation of unacceptable material (as this Section paragraph 18);

(c) disposal of material (as this Section paragraph 32);

(d) trimming back cutting faces.

Filling of Soft Spots and Other Voids

Item coverage

58 The items for filling of soft spots and other voids shall in accordance with the Preambles to Bill of Quantities General directions include for:

(a) deposition of fill (as this Section paragraph 27);

(b) compaction of fill (as this Section paragraph 45);

(c) formwork (as Section 17 paragraph 14);

(d) treatment of cutting faces;

(e) in situ concrete (as Section 17 paragraph 4).

Removal of Disused Sewers, Drains, Cables, Ducts or Pipelines

Units

59 The units of measurement shall be:

(i) removal of disused sewers, drains, cables, ducts or pipelines ...... linear metre.

(ii) backfilling to disused chambers and cellars ...... cubic metre.

Measurement

60 The measurement of the removal of disused sewers, drains, cables, ducts, or pipelines shall be the summation of the distance along the centre line of the route or as stated in the Contract.

The removal of disused sewers, drains, cables, ducts and pipelines shall only be measured where specifically stated in the Contract.

The measurement of backfilling to disused chambers and cellars shall be the volume of the void directed to be filled.

Itemisation

61 Separate items shall be provided for removal of disused sewers, drains, cables, ducts or pipelines and backfilling in accordance with Part II paragraphs 3 and 4 and the following:

Group		Feature
I	1	Removal of disused sewers, drains, cables, ducts and pipelines and the like of different sizes with one metre or less of cover to formation level.
	2	Removal of disused sewers, drains, cables, ducts and pipelines and the like of different sizes exceeding one metre and not exceeding two metres of cover to formation level and thereafter in steps of one metre.
	3	Backfilling disused chambers and cellars.
II	1	Different types of backfilling.

Removal of Disused Sewers, Drains, Cables, Ducts or Pipelines

62 The items for removal of disused sewers, drains, cables, ducts or pipelines shall in accordance with the Preamble to the Bill of Quantities General Directions include for:

Item coverage

(a) excavation of acceptable material (as this Section paragraphs 16 and 17);

(b) excavation of unacceptable material (as this Section paragraph 18);

(c) excavation of hard material (as this Section paragraph 22);

(d) breaking up beds, haunches and surrounds;

(e) backfilling and compaction;

(f) disposal of material (as this Section paragraph 32);

(g) sealing ends of sewers, drains, cables, ducts and pipelines;

(h) credit value of materials.

Backfilling to Disused Chambers and Cellars

63 The items for backfilling to disused chambers and cellars shall in accordance with the Preamble to Bill of Quantities General Directions include for:

Item coverage

(a) compaction;

(b) drainage holes in underground chambers and cellars and cleaning;

(c) grouting;

(d) in situ concrete (as Section 16 paragraph 4).

(e) reinforcement (as Section 16 paragraph 25);

Supports Left in Excavation

Units

64 The units of measurement shall be:

(i) supports left in excavation...........square metre.

Measurement

65 Measurement shall be the area of face directed to be left with supports in position.

Itemisation

66 Separate items shall be provided for supports left in excavation in accordance with Part II paragraphs 3 and 4 and the following:

Group		Feature
I	1	Supports.
II	1	Timber.
	2	Steel.
III	1	Different types.

Supports left in Excavation

Item coverage

67 The items for supports left in excavation shall in accordance with the Preambles to Bill of Quantities General Directions include for:

(a) struts, walings and the like and working around them.

Topsoiling and Storage of Topsoil

Units

68 The units of measurement shall be:

(i) topsoiling..................square metre.

(ii) permanent storage of topsoil .... cubic metre.

Measurement

69 The measurement of topsoiling shall be the area of the surface to be topsoiled. The measurement of the permanent storage of topsoil shall be the volume of topsoil Class 5A excavated from within the Site and measured in accordance with paragraph 14(a) of this Section less the volume of topsoil calculated from the areas and thicknesses to be topsoiled.

Itemisation

70 Separate items shall be provided for topsoiling in accordance with Part II paragraphs 3 and 4 and the following:

Group	Feature	
I	1	Topsoiling of different thicknesses.
	2	Permanent storage of topsoil.
II	1	Surfaces sloping at 10° or less to the horizontal.
	2	Surfaces sloping at more than 10° to the horizontal.

Note: Group I Feature 2 shall not be identified by any Group II Feature.

Topsoiling

Item coverage

71 The items for topsoiling shall in accordance with the Preambles to Bill of Quantities General Directions include for:

(a) the removal of debris;

(b) taking delivery of imported topsoil;

(c) excavation from stockpile;

(d) loading into transport;

(e) haulage, deposition, spreading, levelling and compaction;

(f) trimming the shaping to levels and contours.

Permanent Storage of Topsoil

Item coverage

72 The items for permanent storage of topsoil shall in accordance with the Preambles to Bill of Quantities General Directions include for:

(a) excavation from stockpile;

(b) loading into transport;

(c) hauling, deposition, spreading, levelling and compaction in permanent storage area;

(d) trimming and shaping to levels and contours.

Grassing

Units

73 The units of measurement shall be:

(i) grass seeding, turfing .... square metre.

Itemisation **74** Separate items shall be provided for grassing in accordance with Part II paragraphs 3 and 4 and the following:

Group		Feature
I	1	Grass seeding.
	2	Turfing.
	3	"Hydraulic Mulch" grass seeding.
II	1	Surfaces sloping at 10° or less to the horizontal.
	2	Surfaces sloping at more than 10° to the horizontal.
III	1	Turfing in two layers.

Grass Seeding and Turfing 75 The items for grass seeding and turfing shall in accordance with the Preambles to Bill of Quantities General Directions include for:

Item coverage

(a) freeing surfaces of areas to be grassed or turfed from stones and other debris and reducing the soil to a tilth immediately prior to grassing;

(b) fertilising including additional plant nutrients;

(c) mowing and clearance of grass cuttings;

(d) pegging and wiring of turves.

Completion of Formation and Sub-formation

Units **76** The units of measurement shall be:

(i) completion of formation, sub-formation .... square metre.

Measurement **77** The measurement of completion of formation shall be the area of the surface immediately beneath the sub base except that where capping is required the measurement shall be the area of the surface of the capping.

The measurement of completion of sub-formation shall be the area of the surface immediately beneath capping, excluding sloping sides and edges.

Completion of formation and sub-formation on Class 1C and 6B material shall be separately measured only when Class 1C and 6B material as such is specifically stated by the Contract to be provided at formation or sub-formation level.

Itemisation **78** Separate items shall be provided for completion of formation and sub-formation in accordance with Part II paragraphs 3 and 4 and the following:

Group		Feature
I	1	Completion of sub formation.
	2	Completion of formation.
II	1	On acceptable material.
	2	On class 1C and 6B material.
	3	On rock in cuttings.

Completion of Formation and Sub-formation 79 The items for completion of formation and sub-formation shall in accordance with the Preambles to Bill of Quantities General Directions include for:

Item coverage

(a) removal of protective layer, mud and slurry;

(b) compaction;

(c) cleaning, trimming, regulating, making good and rolling;

(d) cement bound materials;

(e) excavation, processing, compaction of naturally occurring hard material;

(f) measures to protect formation and sub-formation against deterioration or degredation.

Lining of Watercourses

Units

80 The units of measurement shall be:

(i) lining of watercourses............square metre.

Measurement

81 Measurement of lining of watercourses shall be the permanently exposed face area of the work.

Itemisation

82 Separate items shall be provided for lining of watercourses in accordance with Part II paragraphs 3 and 4 and the following:

Group		Feature
I	1	Lining of new watercourse.
	2	Lining of enlarged watercourse.
	3	Lining of intercepting ditches.
II	1	To inverts.
	2	To side slopes.
III	1	Different types.
IV	1	Different thicknesses.

Lining of Watercourses

83 The items for lining of watercourses shall in accordance with the Preambles to Bill of Quantities General Directions include for:

Item coverage

(a) bedding and compaction;

(b) laying, setting, bedding, jointing, wedging, cutting and pointing;

(c) building in pipes;

(d) concrete (as Section 17 paragraphs 4 and 9);

(e) formwork (as Section 17 paragraph 14);

(f) reinforcement (as Section 17 paragraph 25);

Clearing of Existing Ditches

Units

84 The units of measurement shall be:

(i) clearing of existing ditches .... linear metre.

Measurement

85 The measurement of clearing of existing ditches shall be the length along the centre line of the ditch.

Itemisation

86 Separate items shall be provided for clearing of existing ditches in accordance with Part II paragraphs 3 and 4 and the following:

Group	Feature
I	1 Clearing of existing ditches.
II	1 At different locations.

Clearing of Existing Ditches

87 The items for clearing of existing ditches shall in accordance with the Preambles to Bill of Quantities General Directions include for:

Item coverage

(a) excavation and loading into transport;

(b) haulage and deposition of excavated materials in tips off Site provided by the Contractor;

(c) clearing and removing debris and vegetable growth to tips off Site provided by the Contractor;

(d) trimming side slopes and grading bottoms;

(e) maintaining existing outfalls.

Ground Improvement—Establishment of Dynamic Compaction Plant

Units

88 The units of measurement shall be:

(i) establishment of dynamic compaction plant........ item.

Measurement

89 The measurement of establishment of dynamic compaction plant shall be measured once only to each separate location of dynamic compaction on the Site. Any additional establishment of dynamic compaction plant to suit the Contractors method of working shall not be measured.

Itemisation

90 Separate items shall be provided for dynamic compaction plant in accordance with Part II paragraphs 3 and 4 and the following:

Group	Feature
I	1 Establishment of dynamic compaction plant.
II	1 Different locations.

Establishment of Dynamic Compaction Plant

91 The items for the establishment of dynamic compaction plant shall in accordance with the Preambles to Bill of Quantities General Directions include for:

Item coverage

(a) bringing plant and equipment to the location of dynamic compaction;

(b) erecting and setting up plant and equipment including site preparation, levelling, and access ramps;

(c) moving and setting up plant and equipment at each position including site preparation, levelling and access ramps;

(d) dismantling and removing plant and equipment from the Site on completion.

Ground Improvement—Dynamic Compaction

Units

92 The units of measurement shall be:

(i) dynamic compaction .... linear metre;

(ii) dynamic compaction plant standing time .... hour;

(iii) granular blanket .... tonne.

Measurement

93 The measurement of dynamic compaction shall be the sum of the distances through which the pounder is required to fall. The distance for each drop shall be the vertical measurement from the underside of the pounder immediately prior to release, to the level of the ground beneath the pounder immediately prior to the first drop at that point.

94 The measurement of dynamic compaction plant standing time shall be for the period or periods of standing time ordered by the Engineer. Periods of less than half an hour shall not be measured. Any other standing time due to the Contractor's method of working, necessitated by the process of Ground Improvement provided for in the Contract or other than that ordered by the Engineer shall not be measured.

95 The measurement of granular blanket shall be the tonnage of material certified by the Engineer, and shall be only that material included on delivery tickets which is incorporated within the Permanent Works in the locations to the extent and thicknesses stated in the Contract or ordered by the Engineer.

Itemisation

96 Separate items shall be provided for dynamic compaction, dynamic compaction plant standing time, and granular blanket in accordance with Part II Paragraphs 3 and 4 and the following:

Group	Feature	
I	1	Dynamic compaction.
	2	Dynamic compaction plant standing time.
	3	Granular blanket.
II	1	Trial compaction.
	2	Main compaction.
III	1	Different weight of pounder.
IV	1	Different materials.

Note: The measurement of the Group II and III features shall be confined to Group I feature 1.

Dynamic Compaction

Item coverage

97 The items for dynamic compaction shall in accordance with the Preambles to the Bill of Quantities General Directions including for:

(a) preparation and levelling prior to placing the granular blanket;

(b) pounding;

(c) filling craters with adjacent material and compaction;

(d) keeping earthworks free of water;

(e) compaction of surface after the final pass;

(f) complying with particular requirements and constraints;

(g) keeping records;

(h) extracting buried pounder;

Dynamic Compaction Plant Standing Time

98 The items for dynamic compaction plant standing time shall in accordance with the Preambles to the Bill of Quantities General Directions include for:

Item coverage

(a) ancillary plant;

(b) equipment and operatives;

(c) periods of less than half an hour.

Granular Blanket

99 The items for granular blanket shall in accordance with the Preambles to Bill of Quantities General Directions include for:

(a) deposition of fill (as this Section paragraph 27);

(b) compaction of fill (as this Section paragraph 45);

Gabion Walling and Mattresses

Units

100 The units of measurement shall be:–

(i) gabion walling, mattresses .... cubic metres.

Measurement

101 The measurement of gabion walling and mattresses shall be the volume contained within the outline of the gabions or mattresses as stated in the Contract.

Itemisation

102 Separate items shall be provided for gabion walling and mattresses in accordance with Part II paragraphs 3 and 4 and the following:–

Group	Feature	
I	1	Gabion walling.
	2	Mattresses.
II	1	Different mesh materials.
III	1	Different mesh size.
IV	1	Different types of fill.
V	1	Mattresses installed at 10° or less to the horizontal.
	2	Mattresses installed at more than 10° to the horizontal.
VI	1	In noise mounds.

Gabion Walling and Mattresses

103 The items for gabion walling and mattresses shall in accordance with the Preambles to Bill of Quantities General Directions include for:

Item coverage

(a) excavation of acceptable material (as this Section Paragraphs 16 and 17);

(b) excavation of unacceptable material (as this Section paragraph 18);

(c) assembling, tying, fixing, staking and tensioning;

(d) fill, compaction and finishes;

(e) mesh including cutting and folding to form special units and shapes;

(f) bracing and wiring lids.

Crib Walling

Units

104 The units of measurement shall be:

(i) crib walling .... square metre.

Measurement

105 The measurement shall be the flat undeveloped area of crib walling. No deduction shall be made for openings within the wall which are part of the modular system, nor for other openings of one square metre or less.

Itemisation

106 Separate items shall be provided for crib walling in accordance with Part II paragraphs 3 and 4 and the following:

Group	Feature
I	1 Crib walling.
II	1 Different types.
III	1 Curved on plan.
IV	1 With a battered face.
V	1 Different finishes.
VI	1 Different infill.

Crib Walling

107 The item for crib walling shall in accordance with the Preamble to Bill of Quantities for General Directions include for:

Item coverage

(a) bedding and jointing;

(b) dowels and pins;

(c) granular infill and compaction;

(d) special units and forming ends and corners;

(e) obtaining manufacturers" certificate and supplying copy to the Engineer;

(f) building in pipes and forming small openings.

Filling and Capping to Mine Working, Well, Swallow Hole and the Like

Units

108 The units of measurement shall be:

(i) filling of mine working, well, swallow hole and the like .... cubic metre;

(ii) capping to mine working, well, swallow hole and the like .... cubic metre.

Measurement

109 The measurement of filling mine working, well, swallow hole and the like shall be the volume of the mine working, well, swallow hole and the like to be filled.

110 The measurement of capping to mine working, well, swallow hole and the like shall be the volume of concrete forming the capping.

Itemisation

111 Separate items shall be provided for filling and capping of mine working, well, swallow hole and the like in accordance with Part II paragraphs 3 and 4 and the following:

Group	Feature
I	1 Filling.
	2 Capping.
II	1 Mine working.
	2 Well.
	3 Swallow hole and the like.
III	1 Different materials.

Filling and Capping of Mine Working, Well Swallow Hole and the Like

112 The items for filling and capping of mine working, well, swallow hole and the like shall in accordance with the Preambles to Bill of Quantities General Directions including for:

Item coverage

(a) excavation of acceptable material (as this Section paragraphs 16 and 17);

(b) excavation of unacceptable material (as this Section paragraph 18);

(c) backfilling and compaction;

(d) concrete (as Section 17 paragraphs 4 and 9);

(e) formwork including permanent formwork (as Section 17 paragraph 14);

(f) reinforcement (as Section 17 paragraph 25);

(g) flushing;

(h) disposal of material (as this Section paragraph 32);

(i) investigation, inspection and monitoring.

Ground Anchorages—Ground Anchorage Plant

Units

113 The units of measurement shall be:

(i) establishment of ground anchorages plant .... item.

Measurement

114 The measurement of establishment of ground anchorages plant shall be measured once only to each separate location of ground anchorages on the Site. Any additional establishment of ground anchorages plant to suit the Contractors method of working shall not be measured.

Itemisation

115 Separate items shall be provided for ground anchorages plant in accordance with Part II paragraphs 3 and 4 and the following:

Group	Feature	
I	1	Establishment of ground anchorages plant.
II	1	Different locations.

Establishment of Ground Anchorages Plant

116 The items for the establishment of ground anchorages plant shall in accordance with the Preambles to Bill of Quantities General Directions include for:

Item coverage

(a) bringing plant and equipment to the location of ground anchorages;

(b) erecting and setting up plant and equipment including site preparation, levelling and access ramps;

(c) moving and setting up plant and equipment at each position including site preparation, levelling and access ramps;

(d) dismantling and removing plant and equipment from Site on completion.

Ground Anchorages

Units

117 The units of measurement shall be:

(i) ground anchorages .... linear metre.

Measurement

118 The measurement of ground anchors shall be for the complete anchor assembly and shall be the length from the bottom of the fixed anchor to the bearing face.

Itemisation

119 Separate items shall be provided for ground anchors in accordance with Part II paragraphs 3 and 4 and the following:

Group		Feature
I	1	Ground anchors.
II	1	Different types and capacities.
III	1	Not exceeding 5 metres in length.
	2	Exceeding 5 metres in length but not exceeding 10 metres in length and so on in steps of 5 metres.
IV	1	Trial anchors.
	2	Main anchors.

Ground Anchors

Item coverage

120 The items for ground anchors shall in accordance with the Preambles to Bill of Quantities General Directions include for:

(a) boring, augering, lining, under reaming, removing and disposing of material;

(b) cables, wires or strands with couplers, binders and spacers;

(c) anchorages, bearing plates, reinforcing helices, grout inlets, vents and the like;

(d) applying water under pressure and proving water tightness of boreholes;

(e) flushing borehole, cleaning and preparation;

(f) protective system (as Section 19 paragraph 4);

(g) grouting ground anchors including fixed length and free stressing length;

(h) applying pre-stress in one or more stages;

(i) checking the accuracy of load measuring equipment and adjusting;

(j) taking observations and compiling a record of stressing and grouting operations and supplying one copy to the Engineer;

(k) measures to prove anchor suitability.

Ground Anchors—Waterproofing Anchor Boreholes

Units

121 The units of measurement shall be:

(i) waterproofing of boreholes .... linear metre.

Measurement

122 The measurement of waterproofing of boreholes shall be the total length of waterproofing operation instructed by the Engineer.

Itemisation

123 Separate items shall be provided for waterproofing of boreholes in accordance with Part II paragraphs 3 and 4 and the following:

Group		Feature
I	1	Waterproofing of borehole.
II	1	Standard grouting.
	2	Pressure grouting.

Waterproofing of Boreholes

124 The items for waterproofing of boreholes shall in accordance with the Preambles to the Bill of Quantities General Directions include for:

Item coverage

(a) pre-grouting.

(b) redrilling and applying water under pressure and proving water tightness of borehole.

Instrumentation and Monitoring—Boring Plant

Units

125 The units of measurement shall be:

(i) establishment of boring plant .... item.

Measurement

126 The measurement of establishment of boring plant shall be measured once only to each separate location of boring on the Site. Any additional establishment of boring plant to suit the Contractor's method of working shall not be measured.

Itemisation

127 Separate items shall be provided for boring plant in accordance with Part II paragraphs 3 and 4 and the following:

Group	Feature	
I	1	Establishment of boring plant.
II	1	Different locations.

Establishment of Boring Plant

128 The items for the establishment of boring plant shall in accordance with the Preambles to Bill of Quantities General Directions including for:

Item coverage

(a) bringing plant and equipment to the location of boring;

(b) erecting and setting up plant and equipment including site preparation, levelling and access ramps;

(c) moving and setting up plant at each position including site preparation, levelling, and access ramps;

(d) dismantling and removing plant and equipment from Site on completion.

Instrumentation and Monitoring—Boring Holes

Units

129 The units of measurement shall be:

(i) boring holes .... linear metre.

Measurement

130 The measurement of boring holes shall be the linear distance along the axis of the borehole between the instrument base and the level stated in the Contract.

Itemisation

131 Separate items shall be provided for boring holes in accordance with Part II paragraphs 3 and 4 and the following:

Group	Feature	
I	1	Boring holes.
II	1	Vertical.
	2	Raking.
III	1	Depth not exceeding 10 metres.
	2	Depth exceeding 10 metres but not exceeding 20 metres.

Boring Holes

Item coverage

132 The items for boring holes shall in accordance with the Preambles to Bill of Quantities General Directions including for:

(a) boring holes in any material, including changing bits and tools;

(b) disposal of material (as this Section paragraph 32);

(c) taking measures to deal with the presence of water in the boreholes;

(d) drilling fluid;

(e) standing time including ancillary plant, equipment and operatives;

Instrumentation and Monitoring—Instrumentation

Units

133 The units of measurement shall be:

(i)   installation of instruments .... number;

(ii)   installation of tubing, cabling and the like .... linear metre;

(iii) grouting .... linear metre.

Measurement

134 The measurement of installation of instruments shall be the complete installation. The measurement of tubing and the like shall be the length measured from the instrument to the underside of the screw cap, plug or the like, along the centre line of the trench or borehole.

The measurement of cabling and the like shall be the length measured from the instrument to the base of the instrument hut or cabinet along the centre line of the trench or borehole.

The measurement of grouting shall be the distance from the top of the seal to either the bottom of the trench or to the underside of the screw cap plug or the like whichever is the lower.

Itemisation

135 Separate items shall be provided for instrumentation in accordance with Part II paragraphs 3 and 4 and the following:

Group	Feature	
I	1	Installation.
II	1	Different types of instruments.
	2	Different types of tubing or cabling.
	3	Different types of grouting.
III	1	Length or depth not exceeding 10 metres.
	2	Length or depth exceeding 10 metres but not exceeding 50 metres, and so on in steps of 50 metres.

Installation of Instruments **136** The items for installation of instruments shall in accordance with the Preambles to Bill of Quantities General Directions include for:

Item coverage

(a) recording water levels;

(b) cleaning and keeping hole free of deleterious materials;

(c) connections and joints;

(d) keeping items clean during installation;

(e) sand filters including allowing time for settlement;

(f) removing contaminated water;

(g) recording data and supplying one copy to the Engineer;

(h) proving correct functioning.

Installation of Tubing and Cabling

137 The items for installation of tubing and cabling shall in accordance with the Preambles to Bill of Quantities General Directions include for:

Item coverage

(a) standpipes;

(b) cutting and jointing tubing including fittings and screw caps;

(c) connections and joints;

(d) excavation in any material (as this Section paragraphs 16, 17, 18 and 22);

(e) bedding and surround to cable or tube with approved material;

(f) backfilling and compaction;

(g) marking tape or cable covers;

(h) extra length of cable for connection to monitoring equipment;

(i) twisting and snaking.

Grouting

138 The items for grouting shall in accordance with the Preambles to Bill of Quantities General Directions include for:

Item coverage

(a) mixing and placing grout;

(b) in-situ concrete (as Section 16 paragraph 4);

(c) formwork (as Section 16 paragraph 14;

(d) backfilling and compaction;

(e) disposal of material (as this Section paragraph 32);

(f) cover and frame including bedding and seating;

(g) locks and keys.

Instrumentation and Monitoring—Instrument Hut or Cabinet

Units

139 The units of measurement shall be:

(i) erection, servicing, dismantling of instrument hut or cabinet .... item.

Itemisation

140 Separate items shall be provided for instrument hut or cabinet in accordance with Part II paragraphs 3 and 4 and the following:

Group		Feature
I	1	Erection.
	2	Servicing.
	3	Dismantling.
II	1	Instrument hut for the Engineer.
	2	Instrument cabinet for the Engineer.
III	1	Until completion of the Works.
	2	After completion of the Works.

Erection of Instrument Hut

141 The items for erection of instrument hut shall in accordance with the Preambles to Bill of Quantities General Directions include for:

Item coverage

(a) preparation of site;

(b) foundations, bases and hardstandings;

(c) heating, power, water and lighting services;

(d) security fence and lockable gates;

(e) furnishings and fittings;

(f) locks and keys.

Servicing Instrument Hut

Item coverage

142 The items for servicing instrument hut shall in accordance with the Preambles to Bill of Quantities General Directions include for:

(a) depreciation and maintenance of building, services and fences;

(b) depreciation and maintenance of furnishings, fittings and supplies.

Dismantling Instrument Hut

Item coverage

143 The items for dismantling instrument hut shall in accordance with the Preambles to Bill of Quantities General Directions include for:

(a) receiving back from the Engineer and removing furnishings and fittings;

(b) disconnecting, removing and sealing off disused services;

(c) demolishing and removing off Site instrument hut, hardstandings, fences and gates;

(d) disposal of material (as this Section paragraph 32);

(e) reinstatement of the site.

Erection of Instrument Cabinet

Item coverage

144 The items for erection of instrument cabinet shall in accordance with the Preambles to Bill of Quantities General Directions include for:

(a) preparation of site;

(b) foundations and bases;

(c) power and water services;

(d) locks and keys.

Servicing of Instrument Cabinet

Item coverage

145 The items for servicing of instrument cabinet shall in accordance with the Preambles to Bill of Quantities General Directions include for:–

(a) depreciation and maintenance of cabinet and services;

(b) depreciation and maintenance of fittings and supplies;

(c) servicing.

Dismantling of Instrument Cabinet

Item coverage

146 The items for dismantling of instrument cabinet shall in accordance with the Preambles to Bill of Quantities General Directions include for:–

(a) disconnecting, removing, and sealing off disused services;

(b) removing instrument cabinet off Site;

(c) breaking up and removal of foundations, and bases, and disposal of surplus material;

(d) disposal of material (as this Section paragraph 32);

(e) reinstatement of the site.

Instrumentation and Monitoring—Monitoring Equipment

Units

147 The units of measurement shall be:

(i) monitoring equipment .... item.

Itemisation

148 Separate items shall be provided for monitoring equipment in accordance with Part II paragraphs 3 and 4 and the following:

Group	Feature	
I	1	Monitoring equipment.
II	1	Different types.

Monitoring Equipment

Item coverage

149 The items for monitoring equipment shall in accordance with the Preambles to Bill of Quantities General Directions include for:

(a) installing, commissioning, calibrating and maintaining monitoring equipment in instrument hut or cabinet;

(b) installing, commissioning, calibrating and maintaining monitoring equipment in vehicles for the Engineer;

(c) copies of reports and results and supplying to the Engineer;

(d) instructing the Engineer's staff in the operation and maintenance of the instrumentation;

(e) attendance during measurement carried out by the Engineer;

(f) removing on completion.

Ground Water Lowering

Units

150 The units of measurement shall be:–

(i) ground water lowering .... item.

Measurement

151 The measurement of ground water lowering shall be the complete installation. Ground water lowering shall only be separately measured where ground water lowering as such is specifically required in the Contract.

Itemisation

152 Separate items shall be provided for ground water lowering in accordance with Part II paragraphs 3 and 4 and the following:

Group	Feature
I	1 Ground water lowering.
II	1 Different locations.

Ground water lowering

Item coverage

153 The items for ground water lowering shall in accordance with the Preambles to Bill of Quantities General Directions include for:

(a) preparing, amending and submitting proposals to the Engineer;

(b) installation, operation, maintenance and removal of pumping and wellpointing plant;

(c) making arrangements with owners and occupiers of land temporarily acquired, and cost arising therefrom;

(d) diversion of rivers and the like;

(e) soakaways, lagoons and the like;

(f) measures to safeguard water supplies including liaising with Water Authorities.

Trial Pits

Units

154 The units of measurement shall be:

(i) trial pits .... cubic metre.

Measurement

155 The measurement of trial pits shall be the volume of the void, calculated on the basis of the horizontal area of the bottom of the excavation with the depth being measured from the bottom of the excavation to the level at which excavation is directed to be commenced.

Itemisation

156 Separate items shall be provided for trial pits in accordance with Part II paragraphs 3 and 4 and the following:

Group	Feature
I	1 Trial pits.
II	1 0 metres to 3 metres in depth. 2 0 metres to 6 metres in depth and so on in steps of 3 metres.

Trial Pits

157 The items for trial pits shall in accordance with the Preamble to Bill of Quantities General Directions include for:

Item coverage

(a) excavation in acceptable material (as this Section paragraphs 16 and 17);

(b) excavation in unacceptable material (as this Section paragraph 18);

(c) excavation in hard material (as this Section paragraph 22);

(d) locating, working around and supporting pipes, cables, services, apparatus and the like;

(e) attendance to the Engineer and others for inspection and investigation purposes;

(f) disposal of material (as this Section paragraph 32);

(g) backfilling and compaction;

(h) reinstatement of surfaces.

Section 7: Pavements

Sub-Base

Units

1   The units of measurement shall be:

(i)   sub-base .... cubic metre.

Measurement

2   The measurement of sub-base shall be the volume of sub base measured to the outlines stated in the Contract.

3   No deduction shall be made for openings of 1 square metre or less.

Itemisation

4   Separate items shall be provided for sub-base in accordance with Part II paragraphs 3 and 4 and the following:

Group		Feature
I	1	Each group or type of sub-base.
II	1	In carriageway.
	2	In emergency crossing.
	3	In layby and bus bay.

Sub-base

Item coverage

5   The items for sub-base shall in accordance with Preambles to Bill of Quantities General Directions include for:

(a)   trial areas and trials;

(b)   awaiting Engineer's approval of trial areas;

(c)   making good after sampling and testing;

(d)   protection of material in transit and while awaiting tipping;

(e)   grading, measuring, mixing and depositing materials;

(f)   spreading and compaction;

(g)   cleaning, preparing and working on or up to existing surfaces and features;

(h)   curing and protection;

(i)   edge support;

(j)   maintenance of surface;

(k)   taking measures to protect the sub-grade and sub-base from deterioration due to the ingress of water and the use of constructional plant;

(l)   taking measures to improve the sub-base to protect the sub-base and sub-grade from damage due to the Contractors method of construction and choice of constructional plant;

(m) shaping to cambers, falls and crowns;

Pavement

Units

6   The units of measurement shall be:

(i)   roadbase, lower roadbase, upper roadbase, basecourse, wearing course, concrete slab .... square metre.

Measurement

7 The measurement of roadbase, lower roadbase, upper roadbase, basecourse, wearing course and concrete slab shall be calculated using the width of the top surface of the course or slab.

Note: The width of the "top surface" of the course or slab shall be the width required by the Contract and shall exclude sloping sides or edges.

No deductions shall be made for openings of 1 square metre or less.

Itemisation

8 Separate item shall be provided for roadbase, lower roadbase, upper roadbase, basecourse, wearing course and concrete slab in accordance with Part II paragraphs 3 and 4 and the following:

Group		Feature
I	1	Pavement.
II	1	Roadbase.
	2	Lower roadbase.
	3	Upper roadbase.
	4	Basecourse.
	5	Wearing course.
	6	Concrete slab.
III	1	Each group or type.
IV	1	Different thicknesses.
V	1	Reinforced.
VI	1	In carriageway.
	2	In emergency crossing.
	3	In layby and bus bay.

Roadbase, Lower Roadbase, Upper Roadbase, Basecourse, Wearing Course and Concrete Slab

9 The items for roadbase, lower roadbase, upper roadbase, basecourse, wearing course and concrete slab shall in accordance with Preambles to Bill of Quantities General Directions include for:

Item coverage

(a) trial areas and trials;

(b) awaiting Engineer's approval of trial areas and trials;

(c) making good after sampling and testing;

(d) protection of material in transit and while awaiting tipping;

(e) designing mixes;

(f) grading, measuring, mixing and depositing materials;

(g) air entrainment;

(h) spreading and compaction;

(i) cutting back cleaning, preparing and working on or up to existing surfaces and features;

(j) edge support;

(k) reinforcement (as Section 17 paragraph 25);

(l) waterproof membrane underlay;

(m) chippings, surface dressing, bituminous spray, slurry sealing and resin based treatment;

(n) surface texturing;

(o) formwork (as Section 17 paragraph 14);

(p) making joints;

(q) forming or sawing grooves, cleaning, grit blasting, priming, caulking, temporary and permanent sealing of joints;

(r) longitudinal expansion, contraction, warping and construction joint assemblies, including joint filler and crack inducers, tie and dowel bars, dowel bar caps and sheaths and inspection of dowel bars and corrosion protection to tie bars;

(s) shaping to cambers, falls and crowns;

(t) forming recesses, openings, and bays;

(u) curing and protection;

(v) protection of kerbs, masking and unmasking of drainage channels, chamber covers, gully gratings, expansion joints, and the like;

(w) maintenance of surface;

(x) taking measures to protect the pavement from deterioration due to the ingress of water and the use of constructional plant;

(y) anchorages (including excavation and disposal) and thickening of slab at anchorages for continuously reinforced slabs;

(z) measures required for aftercare and opening the road to traffic;

Regulating Course

Units

10 The units of measurement shall be:

(i) bituminous regulating course .... tonne.

(ii) cement bound regulating course .... cubic metre.

Measurement

11 The measurement of bituminous regulating course shall be calculated from the tonnage of material certified by the Engineer multiplied by the factor stated in the item description for the particular aggregate used.

The tonnage certified by the Engineer shall be only that material included on delivery tickets which is incorporated in the Permanent Works in the locations and to the extent and thickness required by the Contract. Material in excess of the requirements of the Contract and material used for any other purpose shall not be included within the certified tonnage.

12 The measurement of cement bound regulating course shall be the volume of material measured to the outlines required by the Contract.

Itemisation

13 Separate items shall be provided for bituminous regulating courses and cement bound regulating courses in accordance with Part II paragraphs 3 and 4 and the following:

Group	Feature	
I	1	Each group or type of bituminous regulating course.
	2	Each group or type of cement bound regulating course.
II	1	Lower road base.
	2	Upper road base.
	3	Road base.
	4	Base course.
	5	Wearing course.

Note: Each item description which includes Group I Feature 1 shall have in addition a tabulated list of the different constituent aggregate types and their factors.

Bituminous and Cement Bound Regulating Course

14 The items for bituminous and cement bound regulating course shall in accordance with Preambles to Bill of Quantities General Directions include for:

Item coverage

(a) roadbase, lower roadbase, upper roadbase, basecourse, wearing course and concrete slab (as this Section paragraph 9);

(b) weighing, tickets and copies;

(c) material not laid as regulating course.

Surface Treatment

Units

15 The units of measurement shall be:

(i) surface treatment .... square metre.

Measurement

16 The measurement of surface treatment shall be calculated using the width of the top surface to be treated.

17 Surface treatment shall only be measured separately when the Contract requires a separate or additional surface treatment to be applied to the pavement. Surface treatment forming an integral part of any specified group or type of pavement shall not be separately measured.

No deductions shall be made for openings of 1 square metre or less.

Itemisation

18 Separate items shall be provided for surface treatment, in accordance with Part II paragraphs 3 and 4 and the following:

Group	Feature	
I	1	Slurry sealing.
	2	Surface dressing.
	3	Bituminous spray.
	4	Resin based surface treatment.
II	1	Different types.
III	1	Different rates of spread.

Surface Treatment

19 The items for surface treatment shall in accordance with Preambles to Bill of Quantities General Directions include for:

Item coverage

(a) trials and trial areas;

(b) awaiting Engineer's approval of trials and trial areas;

(c) making good after sampling and testing;

(d) designing mixes;

(e) grading, measuring, mixing and depositing materials;

(f) spreading and rolling deposited materials;

(g) making joints;

(h) cleaning surfaces;

(i) tack coats;

(j) protection of kerbs, masking and unmasking of drainage channels, chamber covers, expansion joints, road studs, road markings and the like and obtaining clean markings;

(k) in the case of resin based surface treatment certification of spraying equipment and supplying copy of certificate at monthly intervals to the Engineer;

(l) measures required for aftercare and opening road to traffic;

(m) cutting back, cleaning, preparing and working on or up to existing surfaces and features.

Scarifying, Planing or Burning Off

Units

20 The units of measurement shall be:

(i) scarifying, planing or burning off .... square metre.

Measurement

21 The measurement of scarifying, planing or burning off shall be calculated using the width stated in the Contract. No deductions shall be made for openings of 1 square metre or less.

Scarifying, planing or burning off carried out as part of a repave recycle process shall not be separately measured.

Itemisation

22 Separate items shall be provided for scarifying, planing or burning off in accordance with Part II paragraphs 3 and 4 and the following:

Group	Feature
I	1 Scarifying. 2 Planing off. 3 Burning off.
II	1 Different thicknesses or depths.

Scarifying, Planing or Burning off

23 The items for scarifying, planing or burning off shall in accordance with Preambles to Bill of Quantities General Directions include for:

Item coverage

(a) re-shaping and rolling;

(b) shaping to cambers, falls and crowns;

(c) multiple handling of material;

(d) disposal of material (as Section 6 paragraph 32);

(e) working around drainage channels, chamber covers expansion joints and the like;

(f) ramps.

Repave Recycle Process

Units

24 The units of measurement shall be

(i) repave recycle process .... square metre.

Measurement

25 The measurement of repave recycle process shall be calculated using the width stated in the Contract. No deductions shall be made for openings of 1 square metre or less.

Itemisation

26 Separate items shall be provided for repave recycle process in accordance with Part II paragraphs 3 and 4 and the following:

Group	Feature
I	1 Repave recycle process.
II	1 Different thicknesses or depths.

Repave Recycle Process

Item coverage

27 The items for repave recycle process shall in accordance with the Preambles to Bill of Quantities General Directions include for:

(a) heating;

(b) scarifying, planing or burning off (as this Section paragraph 23);

(c) roadbase, lower roadbase, upper roadbase, base course, wearing course and concrete slab (as this Section paragraph 9);

(d) make up low areas and reprofiling.

Reinstatement of Paved Areas

Units

28 The units of measurement shall be:

(i) Reinstatement of paved area .... square metre.

Measurement

29 The measurement of reinstatement of paved area shall be calculated using the width of top surface to be reinstated.

Itemisation

30 Separate items shall be provided for reinstatement of paved area in accordance with Part II paragraphs 3 and 4 and the following:

Group	Feature
I	1 Each type of paved area reinstatement.
II	1 Different thicknesses or depths.

Reinstatement of Paved Area

Item coverage

31 The items for reinstatement of paved area shall in accordance with the Preambles to Bill of Quantities General Directions include for:

(a) sub-base (as this Section paragraph 5);

(b) roadbase, lower roadbase, upper roadbase, basecourse, wearing course and concrete slab (as this Section paragraph 9);

(c) bituminous and cement bound regulating course (as this Section paragraph 14);

(d) surface treatments (as this Section paragraph 19);

(e) kerbing, channelling and edging (as Section 11 paragraph 4);

(f) footways and paved areas (as Section 11 paragraph 21).

Section 8 is not taken up.

Section 9 is not taken up.

Section 10 is not taken up.

Section 11: Kerbing Footways and Paved Areas

Kerbing, Channelling and Edging

Units

1 The units of measurement shall be:

(i) kerbing channelling and edging .... linear metre.

Measurement

2 The measurement of kerbing, channelling and edging shall be the lengths required by the Contract. No deduction shall be made for gaps of 1 linear metre or less.

Itemisation

3 Separate items shall be provided for kerbing, channelling and edging in accordance with Part II paragraphs 3 and 4 and the following:

Group	Feature
I	1 Kerbing.
	2 Channelling.
	3 Edging.
II	1 Specified permitted alternative materials and designs.
	2 Different materials and designs.
	3 Engineers group reference.
III	1 Straight or curved exceeding 12 metres radius.
	2 Curved not exceeding 12 metres radius.

Kerbing Channelling Edging

4 The items for kerbing, channelling and edging shall in accordance with the Preambles to Bill of Quantities General Directions include for:

Item coverage

(a) trial mixes;

(b) awaiting Engineers approval of trial mixes;

(c) making good after sampling and testing;

(d) excavation of acceptable material (as Section 6 paragraphs 16 and 17);

(e) excavation of unacceptable material (as Section 6 paragraph 18);

(f) excavation of hard material (as Section 6 paragraph 22);

(g) disposal of material (as Section 6 paragraph 32);

(h) in situ concrete (as Section 17 paragraph 4);

(i) formwork (as Section 17 paragraph 14);

(j) reinforcement (as Section 17 paragraph 25);

(k) mixing materials and extruding kerbs;

(l) bedding, jointing, filling and sealing joints;

(m) expansion and contraction joints;

(n) keying of surfaces and tack coats;

(o) surface finishing, curing and protection;

(p) gully gratings and frames;

(q) tie bars;

(r) drainage holes or pipes through concrete;

(s) quadrants, dropper kerbs and other special units;

(t) edge support;

(u) preservation of timber.

Additional Concrete for Kerbing, Channelling and Edging

Units

5 The units of measurement shall be:

(i) additional concrete for kerbing, channelling and edging .... cubic metre.

Measurement

6 The measurement of additional concrete for kerbing, channelling and edging shall be the volume required by the Contract in excess of the standard requirements of the Contract for each type of kerbing, channelling or edging.

Itemisation

7 Separate items shall be provided for additional concrete for kerbing, channelling and edging in accordance with Part II paragraphs 3 and 4 and the following:

Group		Feature
I	1	Additional concrete of different classes or grades.
II	1	To kerbing.
	2	To channelling.
	3	To edging.

Additional Concrete for Kerbing, Channelling and Edging

8 The items for additional concrete for kerbing, channelling and edging shall in accordance with the Preambles to Bill of Quantities General Directions include for:

Item coverage

(a) excavation of acceptable material (as Section 6 paragraphs 16 and 17);

(b) excavation of unacceptable material (as Section 6 paragraph 18);

(c) excavation of hard material (as Section 6 paragraph 22);

(d) in situ concrete (as Section 17 paragraph 4);

(e) formwork (as Section 17 paragraph 14);

(f) reinforcement (as Section 17 paragraph 25);

(g) forming, filling and sealing joints;

(h) surface finishing, curing and protecting;

(i) expansion and contraction joints;

(j) drainage holes or pipes through concrete;

(k) disposal of material (as Section 6 paragraph 32).

Remove from Store and Relay Kerbing, Channelling and Edging

Units

9 The units of measurement shall be:

(i) remove from store and relay kerbing, channelling, edging .... linear metre.

Measurement

10 The measurement for remove from store and relay kerbing, channelling and edging shall be the length required by the Contract. No deduction shall be made for gaps of 1 linear metre or less.

Itemisation

11 Separate items shall be provided for remove from store and relay kerbing, channelling and edging in accordance with Part II paragraphs 3 and 4 and the following:

Group		Feature
I	1	Remove from store and relay kerbing.
	2	Remove from store and relay channelling.
	3	Remove from store and relay edging.
II	1	Different materials and designs.
III	1	Straight or curved exceeding 12 metres radius.
	2	Curved not exceeding 12 metres radius.

Remove from Store and Relay Kerbing, Channelling and Edging

12 The items for remove from store and relay kerbing, channelling and edging shall in accordance with the Preambles to Bill of Quantities General Directions include for:

Item coverage

(a) loading, transporting from store, unloading and positioning for relaying;

(b) replacing items damaged during the foregoing operations;

(c) new materials;

(d) kerbing, channelling and edging (as this Section paragraph 4).

Footways and Paved Areas

Units

13 The units of measurement shall be:

(i) footways and paved areas ....square metre.

(ii) bituminous regulating course .... tonne.

(iii) cement bound regulating course .... cubic metre.

Measurement

14 The measurement of footways and paved areas shall be calculated using the width of the top surface stated in the Contract.

15 In the case of flexible construction where an Engineer's Group reference is given for the whole construction, the total thickness of the combined sub-base, basecourse, wearing course and/or surface dressing shall be stated.

16 In all other cases of flexible construction the thickness of each course shall be stated in the item description except that where a surface dressing is an integral part of any course then the combined thickness of the course and surface dressing shall be stated.

17 In cases of insitu and precast concrete, stone and block paving the thickness of the sub-base, bedding and paving shall be separately stated in the item description.

18 The measurement of bituminous regulating course shall be the tonnage certified by the Engineer being only that material included on delivery tickets which is incorporated in the Permanent Works in the locations and to the extent and thickness required by the Contract.

The measurement of cement bound regulating course shall be the volume of material measured to the outlines stated in the Contract.

19 No deduction shall be made for openings of 1 square metre or less.

Itemisation

20 Separate items shall be provided for footways and paved areas in accordance with Part II paragraphs 3 and 4 and the following:

Group		Feature
I	1	Footways.
	2	Paved areas.
II	1	Different types of construction.
III	1	Different thicknesses.
IV	1	Different sizes, groups or types.
V	1	Surfaces sloping at 10° or less to the horizontal.
	2	Surfaces sloping at more than 10° to the horizontal.
VI	1	Regulating course of different groups or types.

Footways and Paved Areas

21 The items for footways and paved areas shall in accordance with the Preambles to Bill of Quantities General Directions include for:

Item coverage

(a) sub-base (as Section 7 paragraph 5);

(b) edge support;

(c) concrete (as Section 17 paragraphs 4 and 9);

(d) formwork (as Section 17 paragraph 14);

(e) reinforcement (as Section 17 paragraph 25);

(f) trial mixes;

(g) awaiting Engineers approval of trial mixes;

(h) laying to falls;

(i) bedding, jointing and pointing;

(j) straight, circular and radial cutting and fitting;

(k) roadbase, lower roadbase, upper roadbase, basecourse, wearing course and concrete slab (as Section 7 paragraph 9);

(l) compacting;

(m) polythene membrane.

Bituminous and Cement Bound Regulating Course

22 The items for bituminous and cement bound regulating course shall in accordance with the Preambles to Bill of Quantities General Directions include for:

Item coverage

(a) bituminous and cement bound regulating course (as Section 7 paragraph 14).

Remove from Store and Relay Paving Flags and Blocks

Units

23 The unit of measurement shall be:

(i) remove from store and relay paving flags and blocks .... square metre.

Measurement

24 The measurement of remove from store and relay paving flags and blocks shall be the area of the top surface the work stated in the Contract.
No deduction shall be made for openings of 1 square metre or less.

Itemisation

25 Separate items shall be provided for remove from store and relay paving flags and blocks in accordance with Part II paragraphs 3 and 4 and the following:

Group		Feature
I	1	Remove from store and relay paving in footways.
	2	Remove from store and relay paving in paved areas.
II	1	Different types of construction.
III	1	Different thicknesses.
IV	1	Different sizes groups or types.
V	1	Surfaces sloping at 10° or less to the horizontal.
	2	Surfaces sloping at more than 10° to the horizontal.

Remove from Store and Relay Paving Flags and Blocks

26 The items for remove from store and relay paving flags and blocks shall in accordance with the Preambles to Bill of Quantities General Directions include for:

Item coverage

(a) loading, transporting from store unloading and positioning for relaying;

(b) replacing items damaged during the foregoing operations;

(c) modification and new materials;

(d) footways and paved areas (as this Section paragraph 21).

Section 12: Traffic Signs and Road Markings

Traffic Signs

Units

1 The unit of measurement shall be:

(i) traffic signs .... number.

Itemisation

2 Separate items shall be provided for traffic signs in accordance with Part II paragraphs 3 and 4 and the following:

Group	Feature
I	1 Permanent traffic signs. 2 Engineer's temporary traffic signs.
II	1 Retroreflective. 2 Non retroreflective.
III	1 Lit sign units. 2 Non lit sign units.
IV	1 Different types.
V	1 Different sizes.
VI	1 Different posts or supports.

Permanent Traffic Signs

3 The items for permanent traffic signs shall in accordance with the Preambles to Bill of Quantities General Directions include for:

Item coverage

(a) excavation of acceptable material (as Section 6 paragraphs 16 and 17);

(b) excavation of unacceptable material (as Section 6 paragraph 18);

(c) excavation of hard material (as Section 6 paragraph 22);

(d) backfilling and compaction;

(e) in situ concrete (as Section 17 paragraph 4);

(f) formwork (as Section 17 paragraph 14);

(g) reinforcement (as Section 17 paragraph 25);

(h) ducts in bases;

(i) reinstatement of surfaces;

(j) temporary covering of signs;

(k) disposal of material (as Section 6 paragraph 32);

(l) locks and keys;

(m) location lettering and marking;

(n) drilling or forming holes and pockets in structures or foundations and casting in bolts sockets base plates and anchorage assemblies;

(o) bedding and grouting;

(p) protective system (as Section 19 paragraph 4);

(q) rivets, bolts, nuts and the like;

(r) electrical equipment, wiring, and connections, excluding network cabling;

(s) conduit including screwed and threaded connections, bends, tees, and the like and draw wires;

(t) threading cable through ducts sleeves, conduit and the like;

(u) backboard;

(v) complying with IEE wiring regulations, earthing, and inspection;

(w) protective treatment;

(x) notices and recording;

(y) preparation and supply of record drawings.

Engineers Temporary Signs

4   The items for Engineers temporary signs shall in accordance with the Preambles to Bill of Quantities General Directions include for:

Item coverage

(a) permanent traffic signs (as this Section paragraph 3);

(b) take up or down and set aside for reuse or remove to store off Site (as Section 2 paragraph 10(a) to (m).

Remove from Store and Re-erect Traffic Signs

Units

5   The units of measurement shall be:

(i) remove from store and re-erect traffic signs .... number.

Itemisation

6   Separate items shall be provided for remove from store and re-erect traffic signs in accordance with Part II paragraphs 3 and 4 and the following:

Group		Feature
I	1	Remove from store and re-erect traffic signs.
II	1	Retroreflective.
	2	Non retroreflective.
III	1	Lit sign units.
	2	Non lit sign units.
IV	1	Different types.
V	1	Different sizes.
VI	1	Different posts or supports.

Remove from Store and Re-erect Traffic Signs

7   The items for remove from store and re-erect traffic signs shall in accordance with the Preambles to Bill of Quantities General Directions include for:

Item coverage

(a) loading, transporting from store, unloading and positioning for re-erection;

(b) replacing items damaged during the foregoing operations;

(c) modification and new materials;

(d) painting existing painted items;

(e) permanent traffic signs (as this Section, paragraph 3).

Road Markings

Units

8 The units of measurement shall be:

(i) marking and removal of solid areas .... square metre.

(ii) marking and removal of lines .... linear metre.

(iii) marking and removal of triangles, circles with enclosing arrows, arrows, kerb markings, letters and numerals .... number. (The Diagram number from the Traffic Signs Regulations and General Directions to be stated.)

Measurement

9 The measurement of the removal of road markings shall only be measured where specifically required by the Contract.

The marking and removal of solid areas shall only be measured for the solid infilling between converging lines, the enclosing lines themselves shall be measured as lines.

Road markings which form part of a traffic signal installation or a pedestrian crossing shall not be separately measured.

10 Markings other than those measured under sub-paragraphs 8(i) and (iii) above shall be measured as lines and shall be grouped together according to width.

In the case of intermittent lines the measurement shall be of the marks only but the length of the mark and gap shall be stated. Double lines shall be measured as two single lines.

Diagonal lines between double lines and short transverse lines at the ends of any longitudinal lines shall be measured with the lines of which they form part.

Ancillary lines shall include lines forming hatched areas, chevrons, zigzag lines and boxed areas (including their enclosing lines). In the case of hatched areas and chevrons the enclosing lines shall be measured with the longitudinal line of which they form part. The measurement of zigzag lines shall include any transverse or longitudinal lines at their ends.

11 The measurement of circles with enclosing arrows (mini roundabouts) shall be for the complete marking, the external diameter of the circle being stated. Distinction shall be made for all other arrows between straight, curved, turning or double headed.

12 Kerb markings shall be measured as a single item irrespective of the number of lines forming any one marking.

13 Each letter or numeral shall be separately measured with all letters or numerals grouped together according to height.

Itemisation

14 Separate items shall be provided for marking and removal of road markings in accordance with Part II paragraphs 3 and 4 and the following:

Group	Feature	
I	1	Removal of road markings.
	2	Road markings.
II	1	Solid areas.
	2	Continuous lines.
	3	Intermittent lines.
	4	Ancillary lines.
	5	Triangles.
	6	Circle with enclosing arrows.
	7	Arrows.
	8	Kerb markings.
	9	Letters and Numerals.
III	1	Different materials.

Group		Feature
IV	1	Different widths of lines.
	2	Different sizes of circles with enclosing arrows.
	3	Different lengths of arrows.
	4	Different lengths of kerb markings.
	5	Different heights of letters and numerals.
V	1	Different lengths of mark and gap for intermittent lines.
	2	Different diagram numbers for arrows and kerb markings.
VI	1	Different types of arrows.

Removal of Road Markings

15 The items for the removal of road markings shall in accordance with the Preambles to Bill of Quantities General Directions include for:

Item coverage

(a) disposal of material (as Section 6 paragraph 32);

(b) reinstatement;

(c) apostrophies in the case of letters and numerals;

(d) markings down the face of kerbs.

Road Markings

16 The items for road markings shall in accordance with the Preambles to Bill of Quantities General Directions include for:

Item Coverage

(a) cleaning, brushing and drying surfaces;

(b) application of the marking materials including the incorporation of specified reflecting medium;

(c) tack coat;

(d) apostrophes in the case of letters and numerals;

(e) kerb markings down the face of kerbs;

(f) adhesives.

Road Studs

Units

17 The unit of measurement shall be:

(i) road studs .... number.

Measurement

18 The measurement of road studs shall be the complete installation.

Road studs which form part of a traffic signal installation or a pedestrian crossing shall not be separately measured.

Itemisation

19 Separate items shall be provided for road studs in accordance with Part II paragraphs 3 and 4 and the following:

Group		Feature
I	1	Road studs.
II	1	Different sizes.
III	1	Different types.

Road Studs

Item coverage

20 The items for road studs shall in accordance with the Preambles to Bill of Quantities General Directions include for:

(a) cutting or forming holes;

(b) adhesives and grout;

(c) reinstatement of surfaces;

(d) disposal of material (as Section 6 paragraph 32).

Remove from Store and Re-Install Road Studs

Units

21 The units of measurement shall be:

(i) remove from store and re-install road studs .... number.

Itemisation

22 Separate items shall be provided for remove from store and re-install road studs in accordance with Part II paragraphs 3 and 4 and the following:

Group	Feature
I	1 Remove from store and re-install road studs.
II	1 Different sizes.
III	1 Different types.

Remove from Store and Re-install Road Studs

Item coverage

23 The items for remove from store and re-install road studs shall in accordance with the Preambles to Bill of Quantities General Directions include for:

(a) loading, transporting from store, unloading and positioning for re-installation;

(b) replacing items damaged during the foregoing operations;

(c) new materials;

(d) road studs (as this Section paragraph 20).

Traffic Signals Installations

Units

24 The units of measurement shall be:

(i) traffic signals installations .... item.

Measurement

25 The measurement of traffic signals installations shall be the complete installation as stated in the Contract.

Itemisation

26 Separate items shall be provided for traffic signals installations in accordance with Part II paragraphs 3 and 4 and the following:

Group	Feature
I	1 Permanent traffic signals installations. 2 Engineers temporary traffic signals installations.
II	1 Different locations.

Permanent Traffic Signals Installations

27 The items for permanent traffic signals installations shall in accordance with the Preambles to Bill of Quantities General Directions include for:

Item coverage

(a) excavation of acceptable material (as Section 6 paragraphs 16 and 17);

(b) excavation of unacceptable material (as Section 6 paragraph 18);

(c) excavation of hard material (as Section 6 paragraph 22);

(d) insitu concrete (as Section 17 paragraph 4);

(e) backfilling and compaction;

(f) disposal of material (as Section 6 paragraph 32);

(g) detectors and loops;

(h) control equipment;

(i) electrical equipment, wiring, and connections; excluding network cabling;

(j) forming slots, cleaning and sealing;

(k) road markings (as this Section paragraph 16);

(l) notices and recording;

(m) numbering and lettering;

(n) complying with IEE wiring regulations, earthing and inspection;

(o) reinstatement of surfaces;

(p) preparation and supply of record drawings.

Engineers Temporary Traffic Signals Installations

28 The items for Engineers temporary traffic signals installations shall in accordance with the Preambles to Bill of Quantities General Directions include for:

Item coverage

(a) permanent traffic signals installations (as this Section paragraph 27);

(b) take up or down and set aside for reuse or remove to store off Site (as Section 2 paragraph 10(a) to (m));

(c) removal of road markings (as this Section paragraph 15).

Pedestrian Crossings

Units

29 The units of measurement shall be:

(i) pedestrian crossings .... item.

Measurement

30 The measurement of pedestrian crossings shall be the complete installation as stated in the Contract.

Itemisation

31 Separate items shall be provided for pedestrian crossings in accordance with Part II paragraphs 3 and 4 and the following:

Group	Feature	
I	1	Permanent pedestrian crossings.
	2	Engineers temporary pedestrian crossings.
II	1	Different locations.

Permanent Pedestrian Crossings

32 The items for permanent pedestrian crossings shall in accordance with the Preambles to Bill of Quantities General Directions include for:

Item coverage

(a) permanent traffic signals installations (as this Section paragraph 27);

(b) road studs (as this Section paragraph 20);

(c) kerbing, channelling and edging (as Section 11 paragraph 4);

(d) footways and paved areas (as Section 11 paragraph 21);

(e) flashing beacons.

Engineers Temporary Pedestrian Crossings

33 The items for Engineers temporary pedestrian crossings shall in accordance with the Preambles to Bill of Quantities General Directions include for:

Item coverage

(a) permanent pedestrian crossings (as this Section paragraph 32).

(b) take up or down and set aside for reuse or remove to store off site (as Section 2 paragraph 10(a) to (m));

(c) removal of road markings (as this Section paragraph 15).

Marker Posts

Units

34 The unit of measurement shall be:

(i) marker posts .... number.

Itemisation

35 Separate items shall be provided for marker posts in accordance with Part II paragraphs 3 and 4 and the following:

Group	Feature
I	1 Marker posts.
II	1 Different types.

Marker Posts

36 The items for marker posts shall in accordance with the Preambles to Bill of Quantities General Directions include for:

Item coverage

(a) protective system (as Section 19 paragraph 4);

(b) numerals, symbols and reflectorised strips or discs including adhesive;

(c) driving or excavating in any material (as Section 6 paragraphs 16, 17, 18 and 22);

(d) backfilling and compaction;

(e) sockets;

(f) galvanised fixings and fittings;

(g) preservation of timber;

(h) disposal of material (as Section 6 paragraph 32).

Section 13: Road Lighting Columns and Brackets

Road Lighting Columns, Brackets, and Wall Mountings.

Units

1 The units of measurements shall be:

(i) road lighting columns, brackets and wall mountings .... number.

Itemisation

2 Separate items shall be provided for road lighting columns, brackets and wall mountings in accordance with Part II paragraphs 3 and 4 and the following:

Group		Feature
I	1	Road lighting columns and brackets.
	2	Wall mountings.
II	1	Different height of columns.
III	1	Different bracket projections.
IV	1	Different lanterns.
V	1	Different types.

Road Lighting Columns Brackets and Wall Mountings

Item Coverage

3 The items for road lighting columns, brackets and wall mountings shall in accordance with the Preambles to Bill of Quantities General Directions include for:

(a) excavation of acceptable material (as Section 6 paragraphs 16 and 17);

(b) excavation of unacceptable material (as Section 6 paragraph 18);

(c) excavation of hard material (as Section 6 paragraph 22);

(d) rivets, nuts, bolts, shims, washers and the like;

(e) blinding concrete or paving slab;

(f) insitu concrete (as Section 17 Paragraph 4);

(g) formwork (as Section 17 Paragraph 14);

(h) reinforcement (as Section 17 Paragraph 25);

(i) drilling or forming holes and pockets in structures or foundations, and casting in bolts, sockets, base plates and anchorage assemblies;

(j) bedding and grouting;

(k) backfilling and compaction;

(l) protective system (as section 19 paragraph 4);

(m) marking and lettering;

(n) electrical equipment for road lighting, wiring and making connections, excluding network cabling;

(o) preparation and supply of data sheets;

(p) disposal of material (as Section 6 paragraph 32);

(q) reinstatment of surfaces;

(r) plugging cable entry slot;

(s) locks and keys;

(t) ducts in bases;

(u) conduit including all purpose made screwed and threaded connections, bends, tees and the like and draw wires;

(v) threading cable through ducts, sleeves, conduit and the like;

(w) backboard;

(x) complying with IEE wiring regulations, earthing and inspection;

(y) protective treatment;

(z) notices, recording and preparation and supply of record drawings.

Remove from Store and Re-Erect Road Lighting Columns, Brackets, and Wall Mountings

Units

4 The units of measurement shall be:

(i) remove from store and re-erect road lighting columns brackets and wall mountings .... number.

Itemisation

5 Separate items shall be provided for remove from store and re-erect road lighting columns brackets and wall mountings in accordance with Part II paragraphs 3 and 4 and the following:

Group	Feature	
I	1	Remove from store and re-erect road lighting columns and brackets.
	2	Remove from store and re-erect wall mountings.
II	1	Different height of columns.
III	1	Different bracket projections.
IV	1	Different lanterns.
V	1	Different types.

Remove from Store and Re-Erect Road Lighting Columns Brackets and Wall Mountings

Item coverage

6 The items for remove from store and re-erect road lighting columns, brackets and wall mountings shall in accordance with the Preambles to Bill of Quantities General Directions include for:

(a) loading, transporting from store, unloading and positioning for re-erection;

(b) replacing items damaged during the foregoing operations;

(c) modification and new materials;

(d) painting existing painted items;

(e) road lighting columns, brackets and wall mountings (as this Section paragraph 3).

Section 14: Electrical Work for Road Lighting and Traffic Signs

Cabling

Units

1 The unit of measurement shall be:

(i) trench for cable .... linear metre.

(ii) cable .... linear metre.

Measurement

2 The measurement of trench for cable shall be the summation of the distance along the centre line of the route between the following points:

(a) face of foundation to road lighting column, lit sign unit, feeder pillar and the like;

(b) the intersection of the centre line of trenches at trench junctions;

(c) the position of trench terminations shown in the Contract.

The measurement of trench for cable shall be measured once only irrespective of the number of cables in the trench.

3 The measurement of cables shall be the summation of their individual lengths along the centre line of the route between the points of cable termination at each item of equipment.

4 Points of cable termination shall be:

(a) in the case of loop detector feeders—the point at which the cable enters the terminal block; and

(b) in all other cases—the point at which the cables enter the boxes, distributors and the like.

Itemisation

5 Separate items shall be provided for cabling in accordance with Part II paragraphs 3 and 4 and the following:

Group	Feature
I	1 Trench for cable, depth not exceeding 1.5 metres. 2 Cable.
II	1 Different widths of trench. 2 Different types and sizes of cable.

Trench for Cable

Item Coverage

6 The items for trench for cable shall in accordance with the Preambles to Bill of Quantities General Directions include for:

(a) excavation of acceptable material (as Section 6 paragraphs 16 and 17);

(b) excavation of unacceptable material (as Section 6 paragraph 18);

(c) excavation of hard material (as Section 6 paragraph 22);

(d) additional depth of excavation to ends of ducts and to maintain specified cover at obstructions;

(e) locating, working around and supporting pipes, cables, services, apparatus and the like;

(f) trimming levelling and compacting;

(g) cable bedding and covering;

(h) backfilling and compaction;

(i) troughing;

(j) disposal of material (as Section 6 paragraph 32);

(k) marking tape or cable covers;

(l) reinstatement of surfaces.

Cable

Item Coverage

7 The items for cable shall in accordance with the Preambles to Bill of Quantities General Directions include for:

(a) extra length of cable required for connection into a unit;

(b) unsealing, clearing and swabbing out ducts, drawing cables through, replacing draw ropes and resealing duct ends and marking;

(c) intermediate supports and fixing devices where cables leave trench and prior to entry into equipment;

(d) sealing to cable ends;

(e) unscheduled joints;

(f) inspection;

(g) marker blocks;

(h) twisting and snaking;

(i) preparation and supply of record drawings.

Cable Joints and Terminations

Units

8 The units of measurement shall be:

(i) cable joints, cable terminations .... number.

Itemisation

9 Separate items shall be provided for cable joints and cable terminations in accordance with Part II paragraphs 3 and 4 and the following:

Group	Feature	
I	1	Cable joint.
	2	Cable termination.
II	1	Different types.
III	1	Different sizes.

Cable Joints and Cable Terminations

Item Coverage

10 The items for cable joints and cable terminations shall in accordance with the Preambles to Bill of Quantities General Directions include for:

(a) preparing, stripping and cleaning ends;

(b) glands and clamps;

(c) connecting conductors to terminals;

(d) removing "knock outs" and drilling back board;

(e) insulating ends of unused conductors;

(f) bonding;

(g) jointing kits;

(h) numbering and lettering;

(i) complying with IEE wiring regulations, earthing and inspection;

(j) keeping the cable joint free of moisture;

(k) markers;

(l) additional excavation in any material (as Section 6 paragraphs 16, 17, 18 and 22).

107

Feeder Pillars

Units

11 The unit of measurement shall be:

(i) feeder pillar .... number.

Itemisation

12 Separate items shall be provided for feeder pillars in accordance with Part II paragraphs 3 and 4 and the following:

Group	Feature	
I	1	Each type of feeder pillar.
II	1	Supplied by Employer.

Feeder Pillars

13 The items for feeder pillars shall in accordance with the Preambles to Bill of Quantities General Directions include for:

Item Coverage

(a) excavation of acceptable material (as Section 6 paragraphs 16 and 17);

(b) excavation of unacceptable material (as Section 6 paragraph 18);

(c) excavation in hard material (as Section 6 paragraph 22);

(d) backfilling and compaction;

(e) disposal of material (as Section 6 paragraph 32);

(f) in situ concrete (as Section 17 paragraph 4);

(g) formwork (as Section 17 paragraph 14);

(h) reinforcement (as Section 17 paragraph 25);

(i) pea gravel, sand and resin;

(j) bolts and fittings and the like including grouting;

(k) backboards;

(l) electrical equipment, wiring and making connections, excluding electricity board supply;

(m) conduit including screwed and threaded connections, bends, tees and the like and draw wires;

(n) threading cable through ducts, sleeves, conduit and the like;

(o) complying with IEE wiring regulations, earthing and inspection;

(p) locks and keys;

(q) protective system (as Section 19 paragraph 4);

(r) notices, numbering, lettering, recording;

(s) preparation and supply of record drawings.

Feeder Pillars Supplied by the Employer

14 The items for feeder pillars supplied by the Employer shall in accordance with the Preambles to Bill of Quantities General Directions include for:

(a) remove from store;

(b) feeder pillars (as this Section paragraph 13).

Section 15: Motorway Communications

The Method of Measurement Clauses for Motorway Communications shall be those termed Section 5 of the Department of Transport TCC Division's, Motorway Communications Manual, Volume III Model Specification, for the Provision of Basic Cable Networks on New Motorways, with edition date as stated in the Preambles to the Bill of Quantities.

Section 16: Piling and Diaphragm Walling

Piling Plant

Units

1   The units of measurement shall be:

(i)   establishment of piling plant .... item.

(ii)   moving piling plant .... number.

Measurement

2   The measurement of establishment of piling plant shall be measured once only to each structure.

Any additional establishment of piling plant to suit the Contractor's method of working shall not be measured. The measurement of moving piling plant shall be measured once only to each pile.

3   Moving of piling plant shall not be measured for steel sheet piling.

Itemisation

4   Separate items shall be provided for piling plant in accordance with Part II paragraphs 3 and 4 and the following:

Group		Feature
I	1	Establishment of piling plant.
	2	Moving piling plant.
II	1	Precast concrete piles.
	2	Bored cast-in-place piles.
	3	Driven cast-in-place piles.
	4	Steel bearing piles.
	5	Steel sheet piles.
III	1	Different cross section.
IV	1	Trial piling as a separate operation in advance of the main piling.
	2	Main piling.
V	1	Different locations.

Establishment of Piling Plant

Item coverage

5   The items for the establishment of piling plant shall in accordance with the Preambles to Bill of Quantities General Directions include for:

(a)   bringing plant and equipment to the site of the structure;

(b)   erecting and setting up plant and equipment including site preparation, levelling and access ramps;

(c)   dismantling and removing plant and equipment from Site on completion.

Moving Piling Plant

Item coverage

6   The items for moving piling plant shall in accordance with the Preambles to Bill of Quantities General Directions include for:

(a)   moving and setting up plant and equipment at each pile position including site preparation, levelling and access ramps.

Precast Concrete Piles

Units

7 The units of measurement shall be:

(i) precast concrete piles, driving, lengthening, driving lengthened piles .... linear metre.

(ii) stripping precast concrete pile heads .... number.

Measurement

8 The measurement of precast concrete piles shall be the lengths required by the Contract. The jointing of segmental piles shall not be measured.

9 The measurement of driving precast concrete piles shall be the length of each pile measured along the axis from the toe to:

(a) the Existing Ground Level or the level of the underside of the pile cap or ground beam (ignoring any blinding layer) whichever is the lower. Provided that where a particular level is specified from which driving shall commence, then the measurement shall be that specified level; or

(b) the site joint of piles to be lengthened, provided that the site joint after completion of the driving is below the level determined in accordance with the preceding sub-paragraph.

10 The measurement of lengthening precast concrete piles shall be the lengths of the added concrete ordered by the Engineer.

The measurement of lengthening precast segmental piles shall be the length of the added segment ordered by the Engineer.

11 The measurement of driving lengthened precast concrete piles shall be the length from the site joint to the level determined in accordance with sub-paragraph 9(a) above.

12 The length classification for those items listed in sub-paragraph 7(i) above shall be based on the appropriate measured lengths determined in accordance with paragraphs 8 to 11 above inclusive.

Itemisation

13 Separate items shall be provided for precast concrete piles in accordance with Part II paragraphs 3 and 4 and the following:

Group	Feature	
I	1	Precast concrete piles.
II	1	Driving precast concrete piles.
	2	Lengthening precast concrete piles.
	3	Driving lengthened precast concrete piles.
	4	Stripping pile heads.
III	1	Vertical.
	2	Raking.
IV	1	Different types.
V	1	Different materials.
VI	1	Different cross section.
VII	1	Piles not exceeding 5 metres in length.
	2	Piles exceeding 5 metres in length but not exceeding 10 metres and so on in steps of 5 metres.
VIII	1	Trial piling as a separate operation in advance of the main piling.
	2	Main piling.

Precast Concrete Piles

Item coverage

14 The items for precast concrete piles shall in accordance with the Preambles to Bill of Quantities General Directions include for:

(a) precast members, and the like (as Section 17 paragraphs 9);

(b) pile shoes, tapered points, prefabricated joints and joint fitments.

Driving Precast Concrete Piles

Item coverage

15 The items for driving precast concrete piles shall in accordance with the Preambles to Bill of Quantities General Directions include for:

(a) pre-boring or jetting;

(b) handling, pitching and driving to a set or level;

(c) taking observations and compiling the record of each pile and supplying one copy to the Engineer;

(d) moving plant and equipment back and redriving risen piles.

Lengthening Precast Concrete Piles

Item coverage

16 The items for lengthening precast concrete piles shall in accordance with the Preambles to Bill of Quantities General Directions include for:

(a) stripping concrete;

(b) forming connection with the old work including splicing, tying or welding reinforcement;

(c) in situ concrete (as Section 17 paragraph 4);

(d) formwork (as Section 17 paragraph 14);

(e) reinforcement (as Section 17 paragraph 25);

(f) precast members and the like (as Section 17 paragraph 9), joints and fitments;

(g) lost time, moving plant and equipment, standing time and disruption caused by the process of lengthening including waiting for concrete to achieve a specified strength.

Driving Lengthened Precast Concrete Piles

Item coverage

17 The items for driving lengthened precast concrete piles shall in accordance with the Preambles to Bill of Quantities General Directions include for:

(a) driving to a set or level;

(b) taking observations and compiling the record of each pile and supplying one copy to the Engineer;

(c) moving plant and equipment back and driving lengthened pile;

(d) moving plant and equipment back and redriving risen piles.

Stripping Precast Concrete Pile Heads

Item coverage

18 The items for stripping precast concrete pile heads shall in accordance with the Preambles to Bill of Quantities General Directions include for:

(a) cutting off, removing and disposing of surplus;

(b) stripping concrete and exposing the reinforcement;

(c) bending projecting reinforcement.

Cast-in-Place Piles

Units

19 The units of measurement shall be:

(i) pile shafts, empty bores .... linear metre.

(ii) enlarged bases .... number.

(iii) bar and helical reinforcement .... tonne.

Measurement

20 The measurement of pile shafts shall be the length of the pile measured along the axis from the toe of the shoe or the bottom of the excavation, including any enlarged base, whichever is appropriate to the specified level of the concrete pile head.

Where an empty bore is specified above a pile shaft, the length classification of the pile shaft shall be based on the overall bored or driven depth including the empty bore.

21 Empty bores shall only be measured where a particular level is specified from which boring or driving shall commence and shall be the length of empty bore or drive measured from the specified level of the concrete pile head, to that particular commencing level.

22 The mass of plain bar reinforcement to cast-in-place piles shall be calculated on the basis that the nominal density of steel is 0.00785 kilogrammes per square millimetre of cross sectional area per linear metre; the mass of deformed bar reinforcement shall be calculated as the nominal rolling mass of the reinforcement.

Itemisation

23 Separate items shall be provided for cast-in-place piles in accordance with Part II paragraphs 3 and 4 and the following:

Group		Feature
I	1	Pile shafts.
	2	Empty bores.
	3	Enlarged bases.
II	1	Vertical.
	2	Raking.
III	1	Different types.
IV	1	Different materials.
V	1	Different cross section.
VI	1	Pile shafts not exceeding 5 metres in length.
	2	Pile shafts exceeding 5 metres in length but not exceeding 10 metres and so on in steps of 5 metres.
VII	1	Trial piling as a separate operation in advance of the main piling.
	2	Main piling.

Pile Shafts and Empty Bores

Item coverage

24 The items for pile shafts and empty bores shall in accordance with the Preambles to Bill of Quantities General Directions include for:

(a) pre-boring or jetting;

(b) casing or lining;

(c) boring or augering to a given level and removing and disposing of surplus material;

(d) driving to a given set or level with or without pile shoe;

(e) excavation, removal, and disposal of material (as Section 6 paragraphs 16, 17, 18, 22 and 32);

(f) drilling fluid and disposal;

(g) protection to personnel, and apparatus for entering the empty bore for the inspection of pile excavation or inside of pile casing;

(h) taking observations and maintaining the boring or driving record of each pile and supplying one copy to the Engineer;

(i) precautions to prevent ingress of surface water and foreign matter;

(j) in situ concrete and precast members, and the like (as Section 17 paragraphs 4 and 9) and stripping concrete to required level and exposing reinforcement;

(k) taking undisturbed soil samples from the bore at any level;

(l) filling of empty bore and around the top of piles and subsequent removal and disposal.

113

Enlarged Bases

Item coverage

25 The item for enlarged bases shall in accordance with the Preambles to Bill of Quantities General Directions include for:

(a) excavation, including under-reaming, removal and disposal of material (as Section 6 paragraphs 16, 17, 18, 22 and 32);

(b) insitu concrete (as Section 17 paragraph 4);

(c) taking measures required because of the presence of water.

Reinforcement for Cast-in-Place Piles

Itemisation

26 Separate items shall be provided for reinforcement for cast-in-place piles in accordance with Part II paragraphs 3 and 4 and the following:

Group		Feature
I	1	Bar reinforcement of nominal size 16 millimetres and under.
	2	Bar reinforcement of nominal size 20 millimetres and over.
II	1	Helical reinforcement.
III	1	Mild steel.
	2	High yield steel.
	3	Stainless steel.
IV	1	Bars not exceeding 12 metres in length.
	2	Bars exceeding 12 metres in length but not exceeding 13.5 metres and so on in steps of 1.5 metres.

Reinforcement

Item coverage

27 The items for reinforcement shall in accordance with the Preambles to Bill of Quantities General Directions include for:

(a) reinforcement (as Section 17 paragraph 25);

(b) bending projecting reinforcement;

Steel Bearing Piles

Units

28 The units of measurement shall be:

(i) steel bearing piles, driving, lengthening pieces, driving lengthened steel bearing piles .... linear metre.

(ii) welding on lengthening pieces .... number.

(iii) cutting or burning off surplus .... number.

Measurement

29 The measurement of steel bearing piles shall be the length required by the Contract.

30 The measurement of driving steel bearing piles shall be the length of the pile measured along the axis from the base to:

(a) the Existing Ground Level or the level of the underside of the pile cap or ground beam (ignoring any blinding layer) whichever is the lower. Provided that where a particular level is specified from which driving shall commence, then the measurement shall be to that specified level; or

(b) the site joint of piles to be lengthened provided that the site joint after completion of the driving is below the level determined in accordance with the preceding subparagraph.

31 The measurement of lengthening pieces for steel bearing piles shall be the additional length ordered by the Engineer.

32 The measurement of driving lengthened steel bearing piles shall be the length from the site joint to the level determined in accordance with sub-paragraph 30(a) above.

33 The length classification for those items listed in sub-paragraph 28(i) above shall be based on the appropriate measured lengths determined in accordance with paragraphs 29 to 32 above inclusive.

Itemisation

34 Separate items shall be provided for steel bearing piles in accordance with Part II, paragraphs 3 and 4 and the following:

Group		Feature
I	1	Steel bearing piles.
	2	Lengthening pieces for steel bearing piles.
II	1	Driving steel bearing piles.
	2	Driving lengthened steel bearing piles.
	3	Welding on lengthening pieces.
	4	Cutting or burning off surplus.
III	1	Vertical.
	2	Raking.
IV	1	Different types.
V	1	Piles not exceeding 5 metres in length.
	2	Piles exceeding 5 metres in length but not exceeding 10 metres and so on in steps of 5 metres.
VI	1	Trial piling as a separate operation in advance of the main piling.
	2	Main piling.

Steel Bearing Piles and Lengthening Pieces for Steel Bearing Piles

35 The items for steel bearing piles and lengthening pieces for steel bearing piles shall in accordance with the Preambles to Bill of Quantities General Directions include for:

Item coverage

(a) fabrication, (as Section 18 paragraph 6), slinging holes;

(b) protective system (as Section 19 paragraph 4).

Driving Steel Bearing Piles and Driving Lengthened Steel Bearing Piles

36 The items for driving steel bearing piles and driving lengthened steel bearing piles shall in accordance with the Preambles to Bill of Quantities General Directions include for:

Item coverage

(a) pre-boring or jetting;

(b) handling, pitching and driving to a set, level or penetration;

(c) taking observations and compiling the record of each pile and supplying one copy to the Engineer;

(d) moving plant and equipment back and redriving risen piles.

Welding on Lengthening Pieces

37 The items for welding on lengthening pieces shall in accordance with the Preambles to Bill of Quantities General Directions include for:

Item coverage

(a) stripping protective system and preparing the head of the driven pile to receive additional length;

(b) full penetration butt weld between driven pile and additional length;

(c) cleaning the affected area and applying protective system;

(d) lost time, moving plant and equipment, standing time and disruption caused by the process of lengthening;

(e) inspection of welds.

Cutting or Burning Off Surplus

38 The items for cutting or burning off surplus shall in accordance with the Preambles to Bill of Quantities General Directions include for:

Item coverage

(a) cutting or burning off to profile, and dispose of surplus;
(b) cleaning the affected area and applying protective system.

Proof Loading of Piles

Units

39 The units of measurement shall be:

(i) establishment of proof loading equipment .... item.
(ii) proof loading of piles .... number.

Measurement

40 Measurement of the establishment of proof loading equipment shall be measured once only to each structure. Any additional establishment of proof loading equipment to suit the Contractors method of working shall not be measured.

Measurement of proof loading of piles shall be the number required by the Contract.

Itemisation

41 Separate items shall be provided for proof loading of piles in accordance with Part II paragraphs 3 and 4 and the following:

Group	Feature	
I	1	Establishment of proof loading equipment.
	2	Proof loading of piles.
II	1	Piles of different types.
III	1	Trial piles.
	2	Main piles.
IV	1	Maintained load.
	2	Constant rate load.
V	1	Vertical.
	2	Raking.

Establishment of Proof Loading Equipment

42 The items for establishment of proof loading equipment shall in accordance with the Preambles to Bill of Quantities General Directions include for;

Item coverage

(a) bringing plant and equipment to the site of each structure;
(b) erecting and setting up plant and equipment including site preparation, levelling and access ramps;
(c) dismantling and removing plant and equipment from the Site on completion.

Proof Loading of Piles

43 The items for proof loading of piles shall in accordance with the Preambles to Bill of Quantities General Directions include for:

Item coverage

(a) setting up rigs, kentledge, cable anchorages, anchor piles, reference bench marks and the like;
(b) moving and setting up plant and equipment at each position including site preparation, levelling and access ramps;

(c) setting up, operating and maintaining instruments and apparatus required to complete the proof loading;

(d) constructing temporary pile caps and subsequent removal;

(e) applying and re-applying the proof load and releasing;

(f) taking readings, measurements and observations;

(g) preparation and supply of record sheets.

Steel Sheet Piles

Units

44 The units of measurement shall be:

(i) steel sheet piling, driving, lengthening pieces, driving lengthened steel sheet piling .... square metre.

(ii) corner, junction, special steel sheet piles .... linear metre.
Measured extra over steel sheet piling.

(iii) lengthening pieces to corner, junction, special steel sheet piles .... linear metre.
Measured extra over lengthening pieces to steel sheet piling.

(iv) driving corner, junction, special steel sheet piles .... linear metre.
Measured extra over driving steel sheet piling.

(v) driving lengthened corner, junction, special steel sheet piles .... linear metre.
Measured extra over driving lengthened steel sheet piling.

(vi) welding on lengthening pieces .... linear metre.

(vii) cutting or burning off surplus .... linear metre.

(viii) walings, ties .... tonne.

Measurement

45 The measurement of steel sheet piling shall be the plane (not developed) horizontal length along the centre line of the piling multiplied by the length as required by the Contract.

46 The measurement for driving steel sheet piling shall be the plane (not developed) horizontal length along the centre line of the piling multiplied by the depth from the toe to:

(a) the Existing Ground Level. Provided that where a particular level is specified from which driving shall commence, then the measurement shall be to that specified level; or

(b) the site joint of piles to be lengthened provided that the site joint after completion of the driving, is below the level determined in accordance with the preceding sub-paragraph.

47 The measurement of lengthening pieces to steel sheet piling shall be the plane (not developed) horizontal length along the centre line of the piling multiplied by the additional length ordered by the Engineer.

48 The measurement for driving lengthened steel sheet piling shall be the plane (not developed) horizontal length along the centre line of the piling multiplied by the depth from the site joint to the level determined in accordance with sub-paragraph 46(a) above.

49 The length classification for those items listed in sub-paragraphs 44(i) to (v) above shall be based on the appropriate measured lengths determined in accordance with paragaphs 45 to 48 above inclusive.

50 The measurement of welding on lengthening pieces and cutting or burning off surplus shall be the plane (not developed) horizontal length along the centre line of the piling.

Itemisation

51 Separate items shall be provided for steel sheet piles in accordance with Part II paragraphs 3 and 4 and the following:

Group		Feature
I	1	Steel sheet piles.
	2	Corner, junction, special steel sheet piles.
	3	Lengthening pieces to steel sheet piles.
	4	Lengthening pieces to corner, junction, special steel sheet piles.
II	1	Driving.
	2	Welding on lengthening pieces.
	3	Cutting or burning off surplus.
III	1	Walings.
	2	Ties.
IV	1	Different types.
V	1	Piles not exceeding 5 metres in length.
	2	Piles exceeding 5 metres in length but not exceeding 10 metres and so on in steps of 5 metres.
VI	1	In main construction.
	2	In anchorages.

Steel Sheet Piling, Corner, Junction, Special Steel Sheet Piles and Lengthening Pieces to Steel Sheet Piling, Corner, Junction, Special Steel Sheet Piles

52 The items for steel sheet piling, corner, junction, special steel sheet piles and lengthening pieces to steel sheet piling and corner, junction, special steel sheet piles shall in accordance with the Preambles to Bill of Quantities General Directions include for:

Item coverage

(a) fabrication, (as Section 18 paragraph 6), slinging holes, tapered points;

(b) protective system (as Section 19 paragraph 4);

(c) drainage holes and the like up to 200 mm in diameter and make good protective system.

Driving Steel Sheet Piling, Corner, Junction, Special Steel Sheet Piles and Driving Lengthened Steel Sheet Piling, Corner, Junction, Special Steel Sheet Piles

53 The items for driving steel sheet piling, corner, junction, special steel sheet piles and driving lengthened steel sheet piling, corner, junction, special steel sheet piles shall in accordance with the Preambles to Bill of Quantities General Directions include for:

Item coverage

(a) handling, pitching and driving to a set, level or penetration;

(b) moving and setting up plant and equipment at each pile position including site preparation or levelling;

(c) taking observations and compiling the record of the piling and supplying one copy to the Engineer;

(d) moving plant and equipment back and redriving risen piles.

Welding on Lengthening Pieces

54 The items for welding on lengthening pieces shall in accordance with the Preambles to Bill of Quantities General Directions include for:

Item coverage

(a) stripping protective system and preparing the head of the driven pile to receive additional length;

(b) full penetration butt weld between driven pile and additional length;

(c) cleaning the affected area and applying protective system;

(d) lost time, moving plant and equipment, standing time and disruption caused by the process of lengthening;

(e) inspection of welds.

Cutting or Burning Off Surplus

Item coverage

55 The item for cutting or burning off surplus shall in accordance with the Preambles to Bill of Quantities General Directions include for:

(a) cutting or burning off to profile and disposal of surplus;

(b) cleaning the affected area and applying protective system.

Walings

Item coverage

56 The items for walings shall in accordance with the Preambles to Bill of Quantities General Directions include for:

(a) fabrication (as Section 18 paragraph 6);

(b) excavation of acceptable material (as Section 6 paragraphs 16 and 17);

(c) excavation of unacceptable material (as Section 6 paragraph 18);

(d) excavation of hard material (as Section 6 paragraph 22);

(e) backfilling and compaction;

(f) disposal of material (as Section 6 paragraph 32);

(g) protective system (as Section 19 paragraph 4).

Ties

Item coverage

57 The items for ties shall in accordance with the Preambles to Bill of Quantities General Directions include for:

(a) fabrication, (as Section 18 paragraph 6);

(b) excavation of acceptable material (as Section 6 paragraphs 16 and 17);

(c) excavation of unacceptable material (as Section 6 paragraph 18);

(d) excavation of hard material (as Section 6 paragraph 22);

(e) backfilling and compaction;

(f) disposal of material (as Section 6 paragraph 32);

(g) threading, couplings, turnbuckles and the like;

(h) protective system (as Section 19 paragraph 4);

(i) marking and drilling piles and making good protective system.

Diaphragm Walling-Plant

Units

58 The units of measurement shall be:

(i) establishment of diaphragm walling plant .... item.

Measurement

59 The measurement of establishment of diaphragm walling plant shall be measured once only for each diaphragm wall.

Itemisation

60 Separate items shall be provided for diaphragm walling plant in accordance with Part II paragraphs 3 and 4 and the following:

Group		Feature
I	1	Establishment of diaphragm walling plant.
II	1	Different locations.

Establishment of Diaphragm Walling Plant

Item coverage

61 The items for the establishment of diaphragm walling plant shall in accordance with the Preambles to Bill of Quantities General Directions include for:

(a) bringing plant and equipment to the site of the diaphragm wall;

(b) erecting and setting up plant and equipment including site preparation, levelling and access ramps;

(c) moving and setting up plant at each position including site preparation, levelling and access ramps;

(d) dismantling and removing plant and equipment from Site on completion.

Diaphragm Walls

Units

62 The unit of measurement shall be:

(i) diaphragm walls, empty excavation .... square metre;

(ii) steel bar reinforcement .... tonne;

Measurement

63 The measurement of the diaphragm walls shall be the area of the vertical section through the centre line of the wall as required by the Contract. Empty excavation shall only be measured where a particular level is specified from which excavation shall commence and shall be the area of the vertical section through the centre line of the empty excavation between the specified commencing level and the finished level of the top of the wall.

64 The mass of plain bar reinforcement to diaphragm walls shall be calculated on the basis that the nominal density of steel is 0.00785 kilogrammes per square millimetre of cross-sectional area per linear metre; the mass of deformed bar reinforcement shall be calculated as the nominal rolling mass of the reinforcement.

Itemisation

65 Separate items shall be provided for diaphragm walls in accordance with Part II paragraphs 3 and 4 and the following:

Group		Feature
I	1	Diaphragm walls.
	2	Empty excavation.
II	1	Different thicknesses of walls.
III	1	Diaphragm walls 0 metres to 5 metres in depth.
	2	Diaphragm walls 0 metres to 10 metres in depth and so on in steps of 5 metres.

Diaphragm Walls and Empty Excavation

Item coverage

66 The items for diaphragm walls and empty excavation shall in accordance with the Preambles to Bill of Quantities General Directions include for:

(a) excavation of acceptable material (as Section 6 paragraphs 16 and 17);

(b) excavation of unacceptable material (as Section 6 paragraph 18);

(c) excavation of hard material (as Section 6 paragraph 22);

(d) backfilling and compaction;

(e) drilling fluid and disposal;

(f) in situ concrete (as Section 17 paragraph 4);

(g) trimming concrete at top of wall;

(h) records and suppling one copy to the Engineer;

(i)   sealing;

(j)   cutting chases, recesses, holes, mortices and the like;

(k)   disposal of material (as Section 6 paragraph 32);

(l)   filling of empty excavation and its subsequent removal and disposal;

(m) guide walls.

Reinforcement for Diaphragm Walls

Itemisation

67   Separate items shall be provided for reinforcement for diaphragm walls in accordance with Part II paragraphs 3 and 4 and the following:

Group		Feature
I	1	Bar reinforcement of nominal size 16 millimetres and under.
	2	Bar reinforcement of nominal size 20 millimetres and over.
II	1	Mild steel.
	2	High yield steel.
	3	Stainless steel.
III	1	Bars not exceeding 12 metres in length.
	2	Bars exceeding 12 metres in length but not exceeding 13.5 metres and so on in steps of 1.5 metres.

Reinforcement for Diaphragm Walls

Item coverage

68   The items for reinforcement for diaphragm walls shall in accordance with the Preambles to Bill of Quantities General Directions include for:

(a)   reinforcement (as Section 17 paragraph 25);

(b)   bending projecting reinforcement.

Section 17: Structural Concrete

In Situ Concrete

Units

1 The units of measurement shall be:

(i) in situ concrete .... cubic metre.

Measurement

2 No deduction shall be made for:

(a) holes, ducts, pockets, sockets, mortices and the like not exceeding 0.15 cubic metres each in volume.

(b) reinforcement;

(c) individual chamfers, splays, rebates, recesses, drips, grooves and the like of 100 mm total girth or less when measured overall the faces of the individual feature formed in the concrete.

(d) in the case of concrete with a patterned profile face, any indentations of 100 mm total girth or less when measured overall the faces of the indentations formed in the concrete.

Itemisation

3 Separate items shall be provided for in situ concrete in accordance with Part II paragraphs 3 and 4 and the following:

Group		Feature
I	1	In situ concrete of different classes or grades.
II	1	Different types of cement.
III	1	Blinding concrete 75 mm or less in thickness.

In situ Concrete

4 The items for in situ concrete shall in accordance with the Preambles to Bill of Quantities General Directions include for:

Item coverage

(a) mix design;

(b) trial mixes;

(c) awaiting Engineer's approval of trial mixes;

(d) mixing, placing in or against any surface, including soil faces, compaction, finishing and unformed surface finishes;

(e) curing and protection;

(f) formwork (as this Section paragraph 14) to upper surfaces inclined at an angle of less than 15° to the horizontal;

(g) trial panels;

(h) awaiting Engineer's approval of trial panels;

(i) falls, cambers, and shaped profiles;

(j) construction joints, (whether or not shown on the Drawings) water bars and stops including formwork (as this Section paragraph 14);

(k) weep pipes, pipe sleeves and the like;

(l) holes, ducts, pockets, sockets, mortices and the like not exceeding 0.15 cubic metres each in volume including formwork (as this Section paragraph 14);

(m) formwork (as this Section paragraph 14) to edge of blinding concrete 75 mm or less in thickness;

(n) filling to over break and working space;

(o) measures to control alkali-silica reaction.

Precast Concrete

Definition

5 The term "precast" applies to a concrete unit cast on Site but not in its final position, and to concrete units manufactured off the Site.

Units

6 The units of measurement shall be:

(i) precast members, slabs, segmental units, hinges, specially moulded blocks, ... number.

(ii) precast copings, capping units plinths and the like of uniform cross section, culverts (excluding piped culverts measured in Section 5 Drainage) .... linear metre.

(iii) precast facing units .... square metre.

Measurement

7 The measurement of precast facing units shall be the plane undeveloped area.

The measurement of culverts (excepting piped culverts measured in Section 5 Drainage) shall be the length measured at the invert level, along the centre line.

The measurement of precast copings, capping units, plinths and the like shall be the measurement along the centre line.

Itemisation

8 Separate items shall be provided for precast concrete in accordance with Part II paragraphs 3 and 4 and the following:

Group	Feature	
I	1	Precast members, slabs, segmental units, hinges, specially moulded blocks.
	2	Precast copings, capping units, plinths and culverts.
	3	Precast facing units.
II	1	Different types.
III	1	Different sizes.
IV	1	Curved.

Precast Members, Slabs, Segmental Units, Hinges, Specially Moulded Blocks, Copings, Plinths, Capping Units, Culverts and Facing Units

9 The items for precast members, slabs, segmental units, hinges, specially moulded blocks, copings, capping units, plinths, culverts and facing units shall in accordance with the Preambles to Bill of Quantities General Directions include for:

Item coverage

(a) mix design;

(b) trial mixes;

(c) awaiting Engineer's approval of trial mixes;

(d) reinforcement (as this Section paragraph 25);

(e) formwork (as this Section paragraph 14);

(f) mixing, placing in or against any surface;

(g) curing and protection;

(h) individual chamfers, splays, rebates, recesses, drips, grooves, and the like;

(i)   holes, ducts, pockets, sockets, mortices and the like;

(j)   matching members;

(k)   marking members for identification and delivery in matching sequence;

(l)   lifting devices including removal and bearing plates;

(m) temporary bracing or stays to prevent displacement;

(n)   trial panels;

(o)   awaiting Engineer's approval of trial panels;

(p)   bedding, jointing and pointing including cramps, dowels or other fixing devices;

(q)   caulking and sealing between and under units and members;

(r)   infilling to joints between adjacent units and members where the maximum width of the joint is less than 150 mm including surface finish and formwork;

(s)   cutting and trimming;

(t)   in the case of precast prestressed members and the like, and in the case of precast and precast prestressed members and the like for incorporation in in situ post tensioned prestressed construction, tendons (as this Section paragraph 31) and stressing (including partially stressing) and grouting internal tendons (as this Section paragraph 32);

(u)   in the case of facing units, units for top, bottom, ends, changes in direction, battering; waterproofing, weep pipes, pipe sleeves and the like.

Surface Finish of Concrete—Formwork

Units

10 The units of measurement shall be:

(i)   formwork .... square metre.

(ii) void formers .... linear metre.

Measurement

11 The measurement shall be the area of formwork which is in contact with the finished concrete but measured over the face of openings of 1 square metre or less and features described in (c) below.

Formwork shall not be measured:

(a)   to construction joints whether shown or not on the Drawings.

(b)   to holes, ducts, pockets, sockets, mortices and the like, not exceeding 0.15 cubic metres each in volume;

(c)   to individual fillets, chamfers, splays, drips, rebates, recesses, grooves and the like of 100 mm total girth or less when measured overall the faces in contact with the concrete;

(d)   to edge of blinding concrete 75 mm or less in thickness;

(e)   to upper surfaces of concrete inclined at an angle of less than 15° to the horizontal;

(f)   to unformed surfaces.

Where concrete, other than blinding concrete 75 mm or less in thickness, is placed in structural foundations, formwork shall be measured to the sides of such concrete foundations regardless of whether or not any formwork is used, except where it is expressly stated on the Drawings that the concrete is to be cast against the soil face.

For measurement of formwork:

(i)   horizontal—shall include formwork horizontal or inclined at any angle up to and including 5° to the horizontal.

(ii) inclined—shall include formwork inclined at any angle more than 5° up to and including 85° to the horizontal.

(iii) vertical—shall include formwork inclined at any angle more than 85° up to and including 90° to the horizontal.

(iv) at any inclination—shall include formwork horizontal or inclined at any angle up to and including 90° to the horizontal.

12 The measurement of void formers shall be the length measured along the centre line of the void former, and shall be measured whether of a permanent or temporary nature.

Itemisation

13 Separate items shall be provided for formwork in accordance with Part II paragraphs 3 and 4 and the following:

Group	Feature	
I	1	Formwork.
	2	Void formers.
II	1	Horizontal more than 300 mm wide.
	2	Inclined more than 300 mm wide.
	3	Vertical more than 300 mm wide.
	4	300 mm wide or less at any inclination.
	5	Curved of both girth and width more than 300 mm at any inclination.
	6	Curved of girth or width of 300 mm or less at any inclination.
	7	Domed.
	8	Void formers of different cross section.
III	1	Different classes of surface finish.
	2	Permanent formwork of different types.
	3	Void formers of different types.

Formwork

Item Coverage

14 The items for formwork shall in accordance with the Preambles to Bill of Quantities General Directions include for:

(a) trial panels;

(b) awaiting Engineer's approval of trial panels;

(c) falsework, centring, fabricating, assembling, cutting, fitting, and fixing in position and taking measures to produce the required shapes of concrete;

(d) forming cambers and falls;

(e) linings and taking measures to produce the required finish to the surfaces of the concrete;

(f) cutting and fitting around projecting members, pipes, reinforcement and the like;

(g) individual fillets, chamfers, splays, drips, rebates, recesses, grooves and the like of 100 mm total girth or less when measured overall the faces in contact with the concrete;

(h) maintaining in place until it is struck and allowing for any variation from the minimum period for striking arising from prevailing weather conditions;

(i) striking, taking down and removing;

(j) concrete provided in lieu of formwork to fill overbreak and working space.

Void Formers

Item coverage

15 The items for void formers shall in accordance with the Preambles to Bill of Quantities General Directions include for:

(a) fixing void formers against displacement during concreting operations;

(b) capping or blocking off ends;

(c) sealing ends and joints.

Surface Finish of Concrete—Patterned Profile Formwork

Definition

16 The term "Patterned Profile Formwork" shall be formwork designed to produce a concrete face with a specified patterned profile comprising ribs, corrugations, troughs or other patterns in relief.

Formwork with a specified regular pattern of formwork joints shall not be classified as patterned profile formwork.

Units

17 The units of measurement shall be:

(i) patterned profile formwork .... square metre.

Measurement

18 The measurement shall be the flat undeveloped area of the patterned concrete required by the Contract but measured over the face of openings of 1 square metre or less and features described in (c) below. Patterned profile formwork shall not be measured:

(a) to construction joints whether shown or not on the Drawings.

(b) to holes, ducts, pockets, sockets, mortices and the like, not exceeding 0.15 cubic metres each in volume;

(c) to individual fillets, chamfers, splays, drips, rebates, recesses, grooves and the like, not forming part of the pattern and of 100 mm total girth or less when measured overall the faces in contact with the concrete;

(d) to edge of blinding concrete 75 mm or less in thickness;

(e) to upper surfaces of concrete inclined at an angle of less than $15°$ to the horizontal.

For measurement of patterned profile formwork:

(i) horizontal—shall include patterned profile formwork horizontal or inclined at any angle up to and including $5°$ to the horizontal.

(ii) inclined—shall include patterned profile formwork inclined at any angle more than $5°$ up to and including $85°$ to the horizontal.

(iii) vertical—shall include patterned profile formwork inclined at any angle more than $85°$ up to and including $90°$ to the horizontal.

(iv) at any inclination—shall include patterned profile formwork horizontal or inclined at any angle up to and including $90°$ to the horizontal.

Itemisation

19 Separate items shall be provided for patterned profile formwork in accordance with Part II paragraphs 3 and 4 and the following:

Group		Feature
I	1	Patterned profile formwork.
II	1	Horizontal.
	2	Inclined.
	3	Vertical.
	4	Curved at any inclination.
III	1	Different types.

Patterned Profile Formwork

20 The items for patterned profile formwork shall in accordance with the Preambles to Bill of Quantities General Directions include for:

Item coverage

(a) formwork (as this Section paragraph 14).

Steel Reinforcement for Structures

Units

21 The units of measurement shall be:

(i) bar and helical reinforcement .... tonne.

(ii) fabric reinforcement .... square metre.

(iii) dowels .... number.

Measurement

22 The mass of plain bar reinforcement shall be calculated on the basis that the nominal density of steel is 0.00785 kilogrammes per square millimetre of cross sectional area per linear metre; the mass of deformed bar reinforcement shall be calculated as the nominal rolling mass of the reinforcement. Steel bar supports to reinforcement where described in the Contract shall be measured as reinforcement.

23 Fabric reinforcement shall be measured as the area of work covered, the BS reference being stated.

Itemisation

24 Separate items shall be provided for steel reinforcement for structures in accordance with Part II paragraphs 3 and 4 and the following:

Group		Feature
I	1	Bar reinforcement of nominal size 16 millimetres and under.
	2	Bar reinforcement of nominal size 20 millimetres and over.
	3	Fabric reinforcement of different BS references.
	4	Dowels of different diameters and lengths.
	5	Helical reinforcement.
II	1	Mild steel.
	2	High yield steel.
	3	Stainless steel.
III	1	Bars not exceeding 12 metres in length.
	2	Bars exceeding 12 metres in length but not exceeding 13.5 metres and so on in steps of 1.5 metres.
IV	1	Bars threaded through holes in members.

Reinforcement

Item coverage

25 The items for reinforcement shall in accordance with the Preambles to Bill of Quantities General Directions include for:

(a) cleaning, cutting and bending;

(b) binding with wire or other material;

(c) supports, cover blocks and spacers (except for steel bar supports to reinforcement where shown on the Drawings);

(d) extra fabric reinforcement at laps;

(e) welding;

(f) mechanical connections.

Dowels

Item coverage

26 The items for dowels shall in accordance with the Preambles to Bill of Quantities General Directions include for:

(a) drilling or forming holes and pockets, casting in and grouting;

(b) protective caps, sleeves and wrappings.

Reinforcement for Reinforced Earth Structures

Units

27 The units of measurement shall be:

(i) vertical rods, strip reinforcing elements .... linear metre.

(ii) sheet, grid, mesh reinforcing elements .... square metre.

Measurement

28 The measurement of vertical rods shall be the length from the top surface of the strip footing to the top of the facing unit or the top of the rod whichever is the higher. The measurement of strip reinforcing elements shall be the overall length including connections and, where applicable, the turn down for end anchorages. Provided that where a strip element comprises of more than one leg measurement shall be of all legs, the number of legs measured being stated in the item description.

Measurement of sheet, grid or mesh reinforcing elements shall be the summation of the areas of each layer.

Itemisation

29 Separate items shall be provided for reinforcing for reinforced earth structures in accordance with Part II paragraphs 3 and 4 and the following:

Group	Feature
I	1 Vertical rods of nominal size not exceeding 16 millimetres.
	2 Vertical rods of nominal size exceeding 20 millimetres.
	3 Strip reinforcing elements of different cross sections or load carrying capacity.
	4 Sheet, grid, mesh reinforcing elements of different references.
II	1 Different materials.
III	1 Vertical rods of different lengths.
	2 Strip reinforcing elements of different lengths.

Vertical Rods

30 The items for vertical rods shall in accordance with the Preambles to Bill of Quantities General Directions include for:

Item coverage

(a) cleaning and cutting;

(b) measures to prevent displacement including adjustments and removal;

(c) protective treatment including tubes and grouting.

Strip, Sheet, Grid or Mesh Reinforcing Elements

31 The items for strip, sheet, grid or mesh reinforcing elements shall in accordance with the Preambles to Bill of Quantities General Directions include for:

Item coverage

(a) examining and checking steel for segregation, laminations, cracks and surface flaws;

(b) cutting, marking off, drilling, notching, machining, bending, connection within the length and preparing for connection to vertical rod facing unit or capping unit;

(c) marking elements for identification;

(d) protective system (as Section 19 paragraph 4);

(e) extra sheeting, grid or mesh at laps;

(f) bolts, nuts, washers and connecting to facing units;

(g) threading over of fixing to vertical rods;

(h) casting in ends to in situ capping units.

In situ Post-tensioned Prestressing for Structures

Units

32 The units of measurement shall be:

(i) tendons, stressing and grouting, protective covering to external tendons .... number.

Definition

33 For the purpose of this Section a tendon is defined as all the permanent components of a system which imparts a compressive load to a concrete member through a common anchorage or bearing plate.

Measurement

34 Lengths of tendons shall be measured along the line of the tendon between the outside faces of those parts of the anchorage units cast into the concrete. Tendons shall be grouped so that no member of the group differs in length from the stated length by more than 5%.

Itemisation

35 Separate items shall be provided for in situ post tensioned prestressing for structures in accordance with Part II paragraphs 3 and 4 and the following:

Group		Feature
I	1	Tendons.
	2	Stressing and grouting internal tendons.
	3	Stressing external tendons.
	4	Final stressing and grouting tendons of members supplied partially prestressed.
II	1	Tendons for in situ concrete construction.
	2	Tendons for segmental construction.
III	1	Tendons of different types.
IV	1	Tendons of different stated lengths.
V	1	Protective covering of different types or size to external tendons.

Tendons

Item coverage

36 The items for tendons shall in accordance with the Preambles to Bill of Quantities General Directions include for:

(a) forming, installing and sealing tendon ducts sheaths and duct formers to profile or between precast segmental units;

(b) steel cables, wires or strands with couplers, tagging, binders, spacers and proving that tendons are free to move between anchorages in ducts;

(c) tendon anchorages, bearing plates, reinforcing helices, grout inlets, vents and other components except where these are supplied complete with precast members or segments;

(d) forming recesses in the concrete for anchorages and jack seatings;

(e) allowing for variations of length in tendons contained in the same bill item;

(f) cutting;

(g) cleaning ducts;

(h) marking grouting and vent points with tendon identification.

Stressing and Grouting Internal Tendons, Stressing External Tendons and Final Stressing and Grouting Tendons of Members Supplied Partially Prestressed

37 The items for stressing and grouting internal tendons, stressing external tendons and final stressing and grouting tendons of members supplied partially prestressed shall in accordance with the Preambles to Bill of Quantities General Directions include for:

Item coverage

(a) checking the accuracy of load measuring equipment and adjusting;

(b) applying pre-stress in one or more stages;

(c) gripping and trimming tendons;

(d) taking observations and compiling a record of stressing and grouting operations and supplying one copy to the Engineer;

(e) in the case of internal tendons, grouting trials, grouting, sealing vent holes and end anchorages, treating ends of tendons and filing anchorages and jack seating recesses with in situ concrete (as Section 17 paragraph 4);

(f) in the case of external tendons, tying or binding to main structure and sealing at joints;

(g) accommodating and adjusting for differences between tendons included in the same bill item;

(h) calculation in respect of the required jacking force and extension;

(i) releasing tension and re-tensioning where pull-in is greater than that agreed by Engineer;

(j) flushing-out of grout.

Protective Covering to External Tendons

Item coverage

38 The items for protective covering to external tendons shall in accordance with the Preambles to Bill of Quantities General Directions include for:

(a) tying or bonding to main structure;

(b) sealing at joints.

Section 18: Steelwork for Structures

Fabrication and Erection of Steelwork

Units

1 The units of measurement shall be:

(i) fabrication, permanent erection .... tonne.

(ii) trial erection at the place of fabrication .... item.

Measurement

2 The measurement shall be the computed weight of the finished member comprising plates, rolled sections, shear connectors, stiffeners, cleats, packs, splice plates and all fittings, without allowance for tolerances for rolling margin and other permissible deviations from standard weights or nominal dimensions, and excluding the weights of welds, bolts, nuts, washers, rivets and protective coatings. No deductions shall be made for notches, cope holes, bolt and rivet holes, and the like; which are each less than 0.03 m² measured in plan.

The computed weight of rolled and cast steel and cast iron shall be determined from the dimensions shown on the drawing, with the addition of 5% to the weight of castings for fillets and overrun, on the following basis:

(a) rolled or cast steel, 7850 kg/m³;

(b) cast iron, 7210 kg/m³.

3 Deck panels shall be measured separately only when the deck panel is not integral with the main member. Bracings, external diaphragms and the like shall be measured separately as subsidiary steelwork only when they are not integral with main members or deck panels.

4 Main members and deck panels shall be inclusive of connectors, stiffeners, internal diaphragms and other integral components.

Fabrication of Steelwork

Itemisation

5 Separate item shall be provided for fabrication of steelwork in accordance with Part II paragraphs 3 and 4 and the following:

Group	Feature	
I	1	Fabrication.
II	1	Main members.
	2	Deck panels.
	3	Subsidiary steelwork.
III	1	Rolled sections.
	2	Plated rolled sections.
	3	Plated girders.
	4	Box girders.
IV	1	Comprised of different combinations of BS 4360 grades of steel.
V	1	Curved on plan or elevation.
VI	1	Tapering.

Fabrication

Item coverage

6 The items for fabrication shall in accordance with the Preambles to Bill of Quantities General Directions include for:

(a) examining and checking steel plate for segregation, laminations, cracks and surface flaws and carrying out any remedial measures required by the Engineer in respect of such defects;

(b) cutting, marking off, drilling, notching, machining, treatment of outside arrises, smoothing to slopes, form fitting, end and edge preparation and cambering.

(c) welding, riveting, bolting, assembling and pre-heating;

(d packing plates, rivets, bolts, including holding down bolts, nuts and washers required to fabricate the steelwork and to complete the erection and installation of steelwork on Site, together with spares and service bolts, drifts, draw up cleats and the like specified in BS 5400 : Part 6;

(e) pre-production procedural trials;

(f) approval testing of welders;

(g) destructive and non-destructive production testing of welding, rivets and shear connectors;

(h) allowance for rolling margins and other permissible deviations;

(i) checking of deviations in rolled and built-up sections and of alignment at joints, including taking measurements and observations and recording and supplying one copy of the record to the Engineer;

(j) preparation and supply of marked erection drawings, marking members for identification and delivery in matching sequence.

Erection of Steelwork

Itemisation

7 Separate items shall be provided for erection of steelwork in accordance with Part II paragraphs 3 and 4 and the following:

Group		Feature
I	1	Trial erection at the place of fabrication.
	2	Permanent erection.
II	1	Different forms of steel sub-structure construction.
	2	Different forms of steel superstructure construction.

Trial Erection at the Place of Fabrication

Item coverage

8 The items for trial erection at the place of fabrication shall in accordance with the Preambles to Bill of Quantities General Directions include for:

(a) temporary bracing or stays to prevent displacement including the provision and removal of temporary attachments;

(b) proving dimensions, cambers and profiles;

(c) match-marking members as required for permanent erection;

(d) dismantling;

(e) modifications and refitting of members as a result of the trial erection;

(f) bolts, sockets, base plates, anchorage assemblies, drilling or forming holes and pockets and casting in.

Permanent Erection

Item coverage

9 The items for permanent erection shall in accordance with the Preambles to Bill of Quantities General Directions include for:

(a) temporary bracing or stays to prevent displacement including the provision and removal of temporary attachments;

(b) approval testing of welders, welding procedural trials;

(c) permanent bolted and welded connections including the provision of preheat and shelters for welding;

(d) checking of deviations at joints, including taking measurement and observations and recording and supplying one copy of the record to the Engineer;

(e) destructive and non-destructive production testing of welding, rivets and shear connectors;

(f) drilling or forming holes and pockets and casting in bars, sockets, baseplates and anchorage assemblies;

(g) adhesives and epoxy or polyester mortar, bedding mortar or grout.

Miscellaneous Metalwork

Definition

10 Miscellaneous metalwork shall comprise items of metalwork incorporated into structures and shall include ladders, brackets, handrails, access covers and frames, mesh panels, walkway panels, screens, grilles and the like.

Units

11 The units of measurements shall be:

(i) miscellaneous metalwork .... item.

Measurement

12 Items of metalwork which are:

(a) included in the computed weight of fabricated items;

(b) included in other measured items; or

(c) separately measured elsewhere

shall not be measured as miscellaneous metalwork.

Itemisation

13 Separate items shall be provided for miscellaneous metalwork in accordance with Part II paragraphs 3 and 4 and the following:

Group	Feature
I	1 Miscellaneous metalwork.
II	1 Different types.
III	1 Different materials.
IV	1 Different sizes.

Miscellaneous Metalwork

14 The items for miscellaneous metalwork shall in accordance with the Preambles to Bill of Quantities General Directions include for:

Item coverage

(a) fabrication (as this Section paragraph 6);

(b) erection (as this Section paragraphs 8 and 9);

(c) protective system (as Section 19 paragraph 4);

(d) in situ concrete (as Section 17 paragraph 4);

(e) formwork (as Section 17 paragraph 14);

Corrugated Steel Structures

Units

15 The units of measurements shall be:

(i) corrugated steel structures (stating the length) ..... number.

Measurement

16 The length stated shall be the extreme length of the corrugated steel structure.

Itemisation

17 Separate items shall be provided for corrugated steel structures in accordance with Part II paragraphs 3 and 4 and the following:

Group	Feature	
I	1	Corrugated steel structures.
II	1	Different types.
III	1	Different sizes.
IV	1	Different thicknesses or gauge.

Corrugated Steel Structures

Item coverage

18 The items for corrugated steel structures shall in accordance with the Preambles to Bill of Quantities General Directions include for:

(a) cutting, marking off, drilling, notching, bevels, skews, bends, edge preparation, cambering, riveting, bolting and fabricating;

(b) marking members for identification and delivery in matching sequence;

(c) laps, rivets, bolts, nuts, washers and the like, spares and service bolts, drifts, draw up cleats and the like;

(d) protective system (as Section 19 paragraph 4);

(e) channels;

(f) awaiting the results of tests.

Metal Facing Units for Reinforced Earth Structures

Units

19 The units of measurement shall be:

(i) metal facing units .... square metre.

(ii) metal capping units and the like .... linear metre.

Measurement

20 The measurement of metal facing units shall be the plane undeveloped area of the facing.

The measurement of metal capping units and the like shall be the measurement along the centre line.

Itemisation

21 Separate items shall be provided for metal facing and capping units in accordance with Part II paragraphs 3 and 4 and the following:

Group	Feature	
I	1	Metal facing units.
	2	Metal capping units and the like.
II	1	Different materials.
III	1	Different types.
IV	1	Different thicknesses or gauge.
V	1	Curved on plan.
VI	1	Built to a batter.

Metal Facing Units and Capping Units

Item coverage

22 The items for metal facing units and capping units shall in accordance with the Preambles to the Bill of Quantities General Directions include for:

(a) fabrication (as this Section paragraph 6);

(b) permanent erection (as this Section paragraph 9);

(c) protective system (as Section 19 paragraph 4);

(d) threading over vertical rods;

(e) sealing joints;

(f) connection to reinforcing elements;

(g) matching as required.

Section 19: Protection of Steelwork against Corrosion

Protective System

Units

1 The units of measurement shall be:

(i) protective system .... square metre.

Measurement

2 The measurement shall be the surface area to be treated.

Itemisation

3 Separate items shall be provided for protection of steelwork against corrosion in accordance with Part II paragraphs 3 and 4 and the following:

Group	Feature
I	1 Protective system.
II	1 Different types.

Protective System

Item coverage

4 The items for protective system shall in accordance with the Preambles to Bill of Quantities General Directions include for:

(a) despatching paint samples to testing authority;

(b) shop procedural trials;

(c) site procedural trials;

(d) masking and other measures to protect adjacent untreated steelwork;

(e) joint fillers and sealing of bolted joints;

(f) preparing materials for application;

(g) preparation of surfaces and coating of steelwork at the place of fabrication and on Site;

(h) complying with any special requirements in respect of ambient conditions for the application of protective treatment and for intervals between successive operations and applications;

(i) stripe coats;

(j) obtaining the correct dry film thickness of paint or other coating;

(k) preparation and supply of system and data sheets;

(l) access, and illumination for inspection.

Section 20: Waterproofing for Structures

Waterproofing

Units

1 The units of measurement shall be:

(i) waterproofing .... square metre.

Measurement

2 The measurement shall be the area of surface covered by the waterproofing. No deduction shall be made for openings of 1 square metre or less.

Itemisation

3 Separate items shall be provided for waterproofing for structures in accordance with Part II paragraphs 3 and 4 and the following:

Group	Feature	
I	1	Waterproofing.
II	1	Different types.
III	1	More than 300 mm wide horizontal or at any inclination up to and including 30° to the horizontal.
	2	More than 300 mm wide at any inclination more than 30° up to and including 90° to the horizontal.
	3	300 mm wide or less at any inclination.
	4	Domed.

Waterproofing

Item coverage

4 The items for waterproofing shall in accordance with the Preambles to Bill of Quantities General Directions include for:

(a) preparing, cleaning and drying surfaces to be waterproofed including levelling courses;

(b) priming, adhesive coats, undercoats and intermediate layers;

(c) laying to cambers, falls and crowns;

(d) protective layers;

(e) additional protection;

(f) formwork (as Section 17 paragraph 14);

(g) additional basecourse or wearing course required as a result of the Contractors choice of waterproofing;

(h) nibs, angle fillets, external angles, mitres, stops and the like;

(i) sealing at edges, chases, and around interruptions and projections;

(j) cutting out and rectifying imperfections;

(k) joints and overlaps;

(l) making good up to abutting surfaces including cleaning and priming;

(m) preparation and supply of data sheets;

(n) preparing and applying bitumen to surfaces of gullies and the like.

Section 21: Bridge Bearings

Bearings

Units

1 The units of measurements shall be:

(i) bearings, installation of bearings .... number.

Measurement

2 The measurement shall be the complete unit.

Itemisation

3 Separate items shall be provided for bearings in accordance with Part II paragraphs 3 and 4 and the following:

Group	Feature
I	1 Bearings.
	2 Installation of bearings.
II	1 Different types.
III	1 Different sizes.

Bearings

Item coverage

4 The items for bearings shall in accordance with the Preambles to Bill of Quantities General Directions include for:

(a) nuts, bolts, washers, dowels, protective caps, dust covers, sockets, sleeves, wrapping, adhesives and lubricants;

(b) surface preparation and protection;

(c) marking bearings for identification purposes;

Installation of Bearings

Item coverage

5 The items for installation of bearings shall in accordance with the Preambles to Bill of Quantities General Directions include for:

(a) drilling or forming holes and pockets and casting in bolts, dowels, sockets, base plates and anchorage assemblies;

(b) forming plinths including formwork (as Section 17 paragraph 14);

(c) setting and releasing locking mechanism;

(d) adhesives and epoxy mortar, cement mortar or grout and surface preparation therefor;

(e) greasing;

(f) alterations to concrete, formwork, reinforcement and the like to suit selected bearings.

Section 22: Parapets

Metal Parapets

Units

1 The units of measurement shall be:

(i) metal parapets, ... linear metre.

Measurement

2 The measurement of metal parapets shall be the developed length along the centre line. The height of metal parapets shall be the height between the top of the top rail and the finished surface level to which the posts are attached or inserted into.

The measurement of concrete parapets shall be in accordance with Section 17 under the heading Precast Concrete.

Itemisation

3 Separate items shall be provided for metal parapets in accordance with Part II paragraphs 3 and 4 and the following:

Group		Feature
I	1	Metal parapets.
II	1	Different types.
III	1	Different heights.

Metal Parapets

4 The items for metal parapets shall in accordance with the Preambles to Bill of Quantities General Directions include for:

Item coverage

(a) fabrication (as Section 18 paragraph 6);

(b) protective system (as Section 19 paragraph 4);

(c) connection pieces for attachment of safety fences.

(d) drilling or forming holes and pockets and casting in bolts, sockets, base plates and anchorage assemblies;

(e) adhesives and epoxy or polyester mortar, bedding mortar or grout;

(f) making good protective system;

(g) infilling;

(h) adjustment to flowing alignment;

(i) fixing to structures.

Section 23: Bridge Expansion Joints and Sealing of Gaps

Bridge Deck Expansion Joints

Definition

1   The term bridge deck expansion joints covers all types of permanent joints which allow expansion, contraction, shrinkage or angular rotation to take place in decks of structures.

Units

2   The units of measurement shall be:

(i)   bridge deck expansion joints .... number.

Measurement

3   The measurement of bridge deck expansion joints shall be the complete installation. The stated length shall be measured along the centre line of the joint.

Itemisation

4   Separate items shall be provided for bridge deck expansion joints in accordance with Part II paragraphs 3 and 4 and the following:

Group		Feature
I	1	Bridge deck expansion joints.
II	1	Different types or materials.
III	1	Different lengths.
IV	1	Different gap widths.

Bridge Deck Expansion Joints

Item coverage

5   The items for bridge deck expansion joints shall in accordance with the Preambles to Bill of Quantities General Directions include for:

(a)   preparing and cleaning surfaces;

(b)   installing or constructing the joint, sub surface drainage, and waterproofing complete with fittings at kerbs, footways, service ducts and the like including the use of templates, guides and the like to retain the joint system in position;

(c)   setting the joint having regard to temperature and other constraints;

(d)   priming surfaces to be sealed, joint filler material, sealing strips, inserting, protecting and sealing;

(e)   adhesives and the like;

(f)   forming, cutting, sealing grooves and edges in road surfacings above joints and sealing;

(g)   protective system (as Section 19 paragraph 4);

(h)   greasing;

(i)   measures to protect the joint against damage or displacement;

(j)   drilling or forming holes and pockets and casting in bolts, sockets, base plates and anchorage assemblies;

(k)   preparation and supply of data sheets.

Sealing of Gaps

Units

6   The units of measurement shall be:

(i)   joint filler .... square metre.

(ii) joint sealant, water bar, water stop .... linear metre.

Measurement

7   The measurement of joint filler shall be the area of the surface to be covered as stated in the Contract.

The measurement of joint sealant shall be the length of the joint on the external face of the sealant.

The measurement of water bar or water stop shall be the length along the axis.
Joint filler and joint sealant shall not be measured to bridge deck expansion joints.

Itemisation

8   Separate items shall be provided for sealing of gaps in accordance with Part II paragraphs 3 and 4 and the following:

Group	Feature	
I	1	Joint filler board.
	2	Joint sealant.
	3	Water bar or water stop.
II	1	Different types or materials.
III	1	Different sizes.
IV	1	Different thicknesses.

Joint Filler

Item coverage

9   The items for joint filler shall in accordance with the Preambles to Bill of Quantities General Directions include for:

(a) cutting and shaping;

(b) preparing, cleaning and priming surfaces;

(c) adhesives and the like;

(d) applying, inserting and casting in filler.

Joint Sealant

Item coverage

10   The items for joint sealant shall in accordance with the Preambles to Bill of Quantities General Directions include for:

(a) preparing and cleaning surfaces;

(b) priming the surface of the joint;

(c) insertion of compressible strip and sealing;

(d) masking and protection;

(e) complying with temperature constraints.

Water Bars or Water Stops

Item coverage

11   The items for water bars or water stops shall in accordance with the Preambles to Bill of Quantities General Directions include for:

(a) cutting, notching, welding, fittings and jointing;

(b) cutting joint filler up to water bar or water stop;

(c) casting in.

Section 24: Brickwork, Blockwork and Stonework

Brickwork

Units

1 The units of measurement shall be:

(i) brickwork .... square metre.

(ii) copings, string courses and the like .... linear metre.

Measurement

2 The measurement shall be the superficial area of brickwork required by the Contract. No deduction shall be made for openings of 0.10 square metre or less.

The measurement of copings, string courses and the like shall be the length of the work required by the Contract.

Note: Facings shall be measured as extra over brickwork except where brickwork is built entirely of facings.

Itemisation

3 Separate items shall be provided for brickwork in accordance with Part II of paragraphs 3 and 4 and the following:

Group		Feature
I	1	Brickwork.
II	1	Copings, string courses and the like of different sizes.
III	1	Different types of bricks.
IV	1	Different thicknesses.
V	1	Different bonds.
VI	1	Different types of mortar.
VII	1	Curved on plan.
VIII	1	With a battered face.
IX	1	In walls.
	2	In facework to concrete.
	3	In arches.
	4	In alteration work.

Brickwork, Copings, String Courses and the like

Item coverage

4 The items for brickwork, copings, string courses and the like shall in accordance with the Preambles to Bill of Quantities General Directions include for:

(a) jointing, pointing and fair-faced work, including rough and fair cutting;

(b) plinths, corbels, bull noses, chases, rebates, quoins and the like, grouting;

(c) ties, dowels, cramps, joggles and the like, including sinkings, mortices and running in;

(d) bonding into existing work;

(e) reinforcement (as Section 17 paragraph 25);

(f) cavity filling between the brickwork and the backing;

(g) building in pipes, holdfasts, bolts and the like and forming small openings;

(h) sample panels;

(i) damp proof courses and membranes;

(j) removing loose material from the backing and washing clean;

(k) curing and protection.

Blockwork and Stonework

Units

5 The units of measurement shall be:

(i) blockwork and stonework .... cubic metre.

(ii) copings, string courses and the like .... linear metre.

(iii) individual blocks, features or stones .... number.

Measurement

6 The measurement of stonework and blockwork shall be the volume of the work required by the Contract.

The measurement of copings, string courses and the like shall be the length of the work required by the Contract.

No deduction shall be made from the measurement for holes or voids of 0.15 cubic metre or less.

Itemisation

7 Separate items shall be provided for blockwork and stonework in accordance with Part II paragraphs 3 and 4 and the following:

Group	Feature	
I	1	Blockwork.
	2	Stonework.
II	1	Copings, string courses and the like of different sizes.
	2	Individual blocks, features or stones of different sizes and shape.
III	1	Different types of construction.
IV	1	Different materials.
V	1	Different types of mortar.
VI	1	Curved on plan.
VII	1	With a battered face.
VIII	1	In walls.
	2	In facework to concrete.
	3	In arches.
	4	In alteration work.

Blockwork, Stonework, Copings, String Courses and the Like, Individual Blocks, Features or Stones

8 The items for blockwork, stonework, copings, string courses and the like, individual blocks, features or stones shall in accordance with the Preambles to Bill of Quantities General Directions include for:

Item coverage

(a) dressed stone facings including in situ dressing;

(b) setting, bedding, jointing, coursing, raking, quoins, grouting, pointing and fair-faced work including rough and fair cutting;

143

(c) bonding into existing work;

(d) ties, dowels, cramps, joggles and the like including sinkings, mortices and running in;

(e) cavity filling between the blockwork or stonework and the backing;

(f) building in pipes, holdfasts, hernbolts and the like and forming small openings;

(g) sample panels;

(h) damp proof courses and membranes;

(i) removing loose material from the backing and washing clean;

(j) reinforcement (as Section 17 paragraph 25);

(k) grooves, rebates, recesses, stoolings and weatherings;

(l) marking for identification and delivery in any matching sequence;

(m) manufacturers certificate and supplying a copy to the Engineer;

(n) curing and protection.

Section 25 is not taken up.

Section 26 is not taken up.

Section 27: Accommodation Works and Works for Statutory Undertakers

The method of measurement for Accommodation Works and Works for Statutory Undertakers shall be in accordance with the various Sections of this Method of Measurement or otherwise as a Provisional Sum.

Printed in the United Kingdom for HMSO
Dd.0296171 4/93 C10 531/3 12521